THE CITY & GUILDS TEXTBOOK

LEVEL 1 DIPLOMA IN
PLASTERING

CW00662566

THE CITY & GUILDS TEXTBOOK
LEVEL 1 DIPLOMA IN
PLASTERING

COLIN FEARN

MIKE GASHE

MICHAEL BLOOM

SERIES TECHNICAL EDITOR
MARTIN BURDFIELD

About City & Guilds

City & Guilds is the UK's leading provider of vocational qualifications, offering over 500 awards across a wide range of industries, and progressing from entry level to the highest levels of professional achievement. With over 8500 centres in 100 countries, City & Guilds is recognised by employers worldwide for providing qualifications that offer proof of the skills they need to get the job done.

Equal opportunities

City & Guilds fully supports the principle of equal opportunities and we are committed to satisfying this principle in all our activities and published material. A copy of our equal opportunities policy statement is available on the City & Guilds website.

First edition 2014

ISBN 978-0-85193-297-2

Publisher Fiona McGlade
Development Editor Claire Owen
Production Editor Lauren Cubbage

Cover design by Design Deluxe
Illustrations by Barking Dog Art and Palimpsest Book Production Ltd
Typeset by Palimpsest Book Production Ltd, Falkirk, Stirlingshire
Printed in the UK by Cambrian Printers Ltd

British Library Cataloguing in Publication Data

A catalogue record for this book is available from the British Library.

Publications

For information about or to order City & Guilds support materials, contact 0844 534 0000 or centresupport@cityandguilds.com. You can find more information about the materials we have available at www.cityandguilds.com/publications.

Every effort has been made to ensure that the information contained in this publication is true and correct at the time of going to press. However, City & Guilds' products and services are subject to continuous development and improvement and the right is reserved to change products and services from time to time. City & Guilds cannot accept liability for loss or damage arising from the use of information in this publication.

City & Guilds
1 Giltspur Street
London EC1A 9DD

T 0844 543 0033

www.cityandguilds.com

publishingfeedback@cityandguilds.com

CONTENTS

FOREWORD

Whether in good times or in a difficult job market, I think one of the most important things for young people is to learn a skill. There will always be a demand for talented and skilled individuals who have knowledge and experience. That's why I'm such an avid supporter of vocational training. Vocational courses provide a unique opportunity for young people to learn from people in the industry, who know their trade inside out.

Careers rarely turn out as you plan them. You never know what opportunity is going to come your way. However, my personal experience has shown that if you haven't rigorously learned skills and gained knowledge, you are unlikely to be best placed to capitalise on opportunities that do come your way.

When I left school, I went straight to work in a butcher's shop, which was a fantastic experience. It may not be the industry I ended up making my career in, but being in the butcher's shop, working my way up to management level and learning from the people around me was something that taught me a lot about business and about the working environment.

Later, once I trained in the construction industry and was embarking on my career as a builder, these commercial principles were vital in my success and helped me to go on to set up my own business. The skills I had learned gave me an advantage and I was therefore able to make the most of my opportunities.

Later still, I could never have imagined that my career would take another turn into television. Of course, I recognise that I have had lucky breaks in my career, but when people say you make your own luck, I think there is definitely more than a grain of truth in that. People often ask me what my most life-changing moment has been, expecting me to say winning the first series of *Big Brother*. However, I always answer that my most life-changing moment was deciding to make the effort to learn the construction skills that I still use every day. That's why I was passionate about helping to set up a construction academy in the North West, helping other people to acquire skills and experience that will stay with them for their whole lives.

After all, an appearance on a reality TV show might have given me a degree of celebrity, but it is the skills that I learned as a builder that have kept me in demand as a presenter of DIY and building shows, and I have always continued to run my construction business. The truth is, you can never predict the way your life will turn out, but if you have learned a skill from experts in the field, you'll always be able to take advantage of the opportunities that come your way.

Craig Phillips
City & Guilds qualified bricklayer, owner of a successful construction business and television presenter of numerous construction and DIY shows

ABOUT THE AUTHORS

COLIN FEARN

CHAPTERS 1 AND 2

I was born, grew up and continue to live in Cornwall with my wife, three children and Staffordshire bull terrier.

As a qualified carpenter and joiner, I have worked for many years on sites and in several joinery shops.

I won the National Wood Award for joinery work and am also a Fellow of the Institute of Carpenters, holder of the Master Craft certificate and have a BA in Education and Training.

I was until recently a full-time lecturer at Cornwall College, teaching both full-time students and apprentices.

I now work full-time as a writer for construction qualifications, practical assessments, questions and teaching materials for UK and Caribbean qualifications.

In my spare time I enjoy walks, small antiques and 'keeping my hand in' with various building projects.

MIKE GASHE

CHAPTERS 3, 4 AND 9

I was brought up in a small village in the Snowdonia National Park, where I continue to live with my family. My plastering career started at the age of 16, attending Bangor Technical College under an apprentice scheme. During my time as a student at the college I won the Blue Circle Apprentice Award as well as the British Gypsum Young Apprentice Award.

Following my time at the college I went on to work as a self-employed plasterer for a number of years. For the past 20 years I have been a lecturer in the plastering section at Coleg Menai, now known as Grŵp Llandrillo Menai. During my time at the college many learners have been successful in a number of national awards and achievements.

I have recently been awarded the Master Plasterer qualification and I am also a freeman of The Worshipful Company of Plaisterers.

MICHAEL BLOOM
CONTRIBUTING AUTHOR

I grew up in London and began plastering aged 16 while still at school. I gained an apprenticeship and attended the Hammersmith and West London College. During my apprenticeship I won the NFBTE and Tilcon award for best apprentice, and achieved my City & Guilds qualification in plastering.

I have worked in the plastering industry for over 30 years, including working in the British film industry and for the British Museum using my fibrous plastering skills. I ran my own company for several years. For the past 10 years I have been living in Suffolk and working at Easton and Otley College as course leader/lecturer for plastering. During my time at the college, the plastering department has won several national awards, including best student for both solid and fibrous plastering. I enjoy passing on my skills and knowledge to the next generation of plasterers.

MARTIN BURDFIELD
SERIES TECHNICAL EDITOR

I come from a long line of builders and strongly believe that you will find a career in the construction industry a very rewarding one. Be proud of the work you produce; it will be there for others to admire for many years.

As an apprentice I enjoyed acquiring new knowledge and learning new skills. I achieved the C&G Silver Medal for the highest marks in the Advanced Craft Certificate and won the UK's first Gold Medal in Joinery at the World Skills Competition. My career took me on from foreman, to estimator and then works manager with a number of large joinery companies, where I had the privilege of working on some prestigious projects.

Concurrent with this I began working in education. I have now worked in further education for over 35 years enjoying watching learners' skills improve during their training. For 10 years I ran the Skillbuild Joinery competitions and was the UK Training Manager and Chief Expert Elect at the World Skills Competition, training the UK's second Gold Medallist in Joinery.

Working with City & Guilds in various roles over the past 25 years has been very rewarding.

I believe that if you work and study hard anything is possible.

HOW TO USE THIS TEXTBOOK

Welcome to your City & Guilds Level 1 Diploma in Plastering textbook. It is designed to guide you through your Level 1 qualification and be a useful reference for you throughout your career. Each of Chapters 1 to 7 covers a unit from the 6708 Level 1 qualification, and covers everything you will need to understand in order to complete your written or online tests and prepare for your practical assessments. Chapters 8 and 9 will introduce you to fibrous plastering and floor screeding, which are covered in the Level 2 qualification.

Please note that not all of the chapters will cover the learning outcomes in order. They have been put into a logical sequence as used within the industry and to cover all skills and techniques required.

Throughout this textbook you will see the following features:

Gaul

A hollow or miss on the surface of the finished plaster

Useful words – Words in bold in the text are explained in the margin to help your understanding.

INDUSTRY TIP

Over mixing or remixing plastering materials affects the setting process and can lead to slow setting or fast setting.

Industry tips – Useful hints and tips related to working in the plastering industry.

ACTIVITY

Work out how long the screws should be to fix up 9.5mm, 12.5mm and 15mm thick plasterboards.

Activities – These are suggested activities for you to complete.

OUR HOUSE

You are about to plaster an internal wall of 'Our House' with a lightweight plaster. However, before you can do this you will need to prepare the timber wall plates that are fitted to the perimeter on top of the blockwork. These are used for fixing the roof trusses, too. Make a list of the materials you will use to prepare the timber wall plates.

'Our House' – These are activities that tie in directly with 'Our House' on SmartScreen to help you put the techniques in the book in context. Ask your tutor for your log-in details.

STEP 1 Mix the different material and include the plasticiser, which will give the mix its workability.

STEP 2 Load the spot board. Next, set up your hop-up. This will give you a platform that allows you to reach the ceiling height of the wall.

Step-by-steps – These steps illustrate techniques and procedures that you will need to learn in order to carry out plastering tasks.

Case Study: Matthew

Matthew is a young trainee plasterer who has been given a job of setting a new plasterboard wall which is 3.5m long and 2.2m high. Although Matthew has worked with experienced plasterers before, this is his first setting job on his own.

Matthew worked out how much finish plaster he requires using calculations and reading the manufacturer's instructions on coverage. He checked the plasterboard for straightness and plumb. He then applied the finish plaster in the correct method, keeping everything clean and tidy as he went along.

Case Studies – Each chapter ends with a case study of an operative who has faced a common problem in the industry. Some of these will reveal the solution and others provide you with the opportunity to solve the problem.

Scabbling 	The removal of the surface finish by mechanical means, producing a suitable key.

Trade dictionary – This feature lists all of the key terms that you will pick up from reading this book.

At the end of every chapter are some 'Test your knowledge' questions. These questions are designed to test your understanding of what you have learnt in that chapter. This can help with identifying further training or revision needed. You will find the answers at the end of the book.

INTRODUCTION

This book has been written to support students studying plastering at Level 1. By studying this book, you should receive a thorough grounding in the skills and knowledge you will need to complete your course and either progress to Level 2, or enter the workforce. You will learn about the wider construction industry and how it works, as well as the skills and techniques you will need in order to work as a plasterer. You will be able to work safely on site using the correct tools and equipment to prepare backgrounds, fix sheet materials and plaster walls to produce a professional finish.

In addition to the features listed on the previous page, which are there to help you retain the information you will need to become a plasterer, this textbook includes a large trade dictionary. Use this for reference in class and in the workshop. Become familiar with the terms and techniques, and pay attention to the skills you need to master. If you put in the effort, you will be rewarded with a satisfying and successful career in construction.

ACKNOWLEDGEMENTS

I would like to thank my dear wife Helen for her support in writing for this book. I dedicate my work to Matt, Tasha and Daisy, and not forgetting Floyd and Mrs Dusty.

Colin Fearn

Firstly I would like to thank City & Guilds and their publishing team for giving me the opportunity to write three chapters for this book. Many thanks to Grŵp Llandrillo Menai for their continued support and to my colleagues in the plastering section, especially Wayne Taylor for his support and advice. Lastly thanks to NAPL members for their support and positive advice while writing the chapters. I would like to dedicate the chapters I wrote to all plastering learners who may benefit from my experience and knowledge of the plastering trade.

Mike Gashe

I would like to thank my children for their understanding and great humour, and Jacqueline for her constant support, patience and encouragement while working on this book. Thank you to the plastering tutors who inspired me, and I hope this book will also inspire new learners. Lastly, many thanks to City & Guilds for the opportunity to pass on my knowledge and experience to a new generation of plasterers.

Michael Bloom

To my gorgeous wife Clare, without whose constant support, understanding and patience I would not have been able to continue. To Matthew and Eleanor, for not being there on too many occasions: normal service will be resumed. Finally, my parents, to whom I will always be grateful.

Martin Burdfield

City & Guilds would like to sincerely thank the following:

For invaluable plastering expertise

Peter Gibson, Mick Glossop, Ian Pollitt and Jason Poole.

For their help with photoshoots

Andrew Buckle (photographer), Brian McDermott, Mike Gashe and all the staff and students at Grŵp Llandrillo Menai.

For supplying pictures for the book cover

Andrew Buckle.

TRADE DICTIONARY

Industry term	Definition and regional variations
Additive Plasticiser	A substance that is added to plaster mixes to change their natural properties. For example, plasticiser is a liquid additive added to the plaster mix to make it workable. Waterproofers and frostproofers are other types of additives.
Adhere/adhesion	How well a material bonds to its background.
Aggregate	A 'filler', aggregate makes up the bulk of a mix. The size and type of aggregate are what determine the mix's strength. Types of aggregate include vermiculite, perlite, granite (shown) and sand.
Approved Code of Practice (ACoP)	ACoP gives practical advice for those involved in the construction industry in relation to using machinery safely. ACoP has a special legal status and employers and employees are expected to work within its guidelines.
Architect	A trained professional who designs a structure and represents the client who wants the structure built. They are responsible for the production of the working drawings. They supervise the construction of buildings or other large structures.
Architectural technician	A draftsperson who works in an architectural practice. They usually prepare the location drawings for a building.

Industry term	Definition and regional variations
Bill of quantities BILL OF QUANTITIES (Assuming Civil Engineering Standard Method of M Number — Item description CLASS A: GENERAL ITEMS Specified Requirements	Produced by the quantity surveyor and describes everything that is required for the job based on the drawings, specification and schedules. It is sent out to contractors and ensures that all the contractors are pricing for the job using the same information.
Binder Cement	The binder is the active ingredient in a mix. It is what sets and holds the aggregate and other materials together. Gypsum, cement and lime are all types of binder.
Bolster with hand protection	There are different types of bolsters used for removing plaster, with various widths of blades. The safer and better ones will have a rubber hand-protector at the head. Bolsters with mushroom heads should not be used as these may chip off and cause injury when in use.
Bond	When the plaster sufficiently adheres to the background surface.
Bonding agents PVA	A bonding adhesive applied with a brush, paddle, small shovel or roller to improve the bond between plaster or render and a background with a poor key.
Bound edge	The long edge of the plasterboard where the lining paper is wrapped up around the sides. *See also* Unbound edge.
Box rule	For ruling in screeds and checking the level.

Industry term	Definition and regional variations
British Standards Institute (BSI)	The authority that develops and publishes standards in the UK.
Broken in trowel 	Describing a well-used or worn trowel which has a more flexible blade, the corners have been rounded off and the edge is sharper. This makes applying finishing coats easier. You can buy 'ready to go' trowels with the edges rounded off to speed up the breaking in period.
Bucket	Buckets have many uses for plastering, including transporting materials and clean water, and for mixing and cleaning. *Regional variation: tub*
Bucket trowel	When mixing is in progress, this tool can be used to clean the rim of the mixing bucket, moving dry unmixed plaster back to the centre of the bucket with its wide, flat edge.
Building Regulations	A series of documents that set out legal requirements for the standards of building work.
Busk	Small rectangular tool used for making good fine jointing and minor defects. These can be different shapes, used depending on the shape and detail of the mould.
Casting	Producing fibrous plasterwork by mixing fine casting plaster and water, then applying the mixed material over or into reverse moulds, to produce a positive mould. Casting is a process that can be completed with either a 'one gauge' or 'two gauge' mix, depending on the size of the cast to be produced.
Casting brush	The casting brush has open bristles that are good for retrieving and applying casting plaster onto reverse moulds. *Regional variation: splash brush*

Industry term	Definition and regional variations
Cement 	Cement is used to bind and provide strength in the plastering mix. It is made from limestone and clay, and is used because of its faster setting time compared with lime mixes. Cement mixed with sand and water will begin to set after 45 minutes and will normally be completely set by the next day.
Class A plaster 	A type of plaster that sets quickly (approximately 20 minutes) and does not contain any retarder, unlike multi-finish plaster, which has a retarder added to allow more working time.
Claw hammer 	This hammer is used when preparing timber backgrounds that have been previously plastered. Its main function is to remove old nails that might be left in the timber surface, or to remove old lath work or damaged plasterboard.
Comb scratcher 	Used to form a key on scratch coats. A comb scratcher is generally used on cement-based plasters. It is similar to a scarifier, but has fewer teeth.
Composite background 	A wall made up of two or more materials, ie brick- and blockwork.
Consolidate 	To close in the surface of a floating coat or floor screed with a float, making it more dense and compact.
Craft knife 	Used for cutting boards. Craft knifes can have fixed blades but, for safety reasons, ones with retractable blades are better. *Regional variations: board knife, utility knife*

Industry term	Definition and regional variations
Crow bar	This is a long bar that can be used to lever materials that are wedged in place. It can also be used to remove stubborn nails and screws.
Darby	This tool has many uses. One is to rule and flatten scratch coat surfaces. Another is to form the angles of returns and reveals on uneven surfaces.
Datum point	A fixed point or height from which to take reference levels. They may be permanent Ordnance bench marks (OBMs) or temporary bench marks (TBMs). The datum point is used to transfer levels across a building site. It represents the finished floor level (FFL) on a dwelling.
Delaminate	To divide or become divided into layers. It indicates a failure of composite materials.
Devil float	A devil float is a plastic float with nails hammered through the top of one end so they stick through the face by 1mm. It is used to provide a key for a setting coat of plaster.
Drill	A small cordless drill is essential to drill pilot holes and secure a running mould, together with suitable screws.
Drill and whisk	A powerful motorised drill with an attached whisk that mixes plaster with ease. It is a fast and efficient way of mixing lightweight plasters.
Drum mixer	A mechanical mixer for mixing materials. Sand and cement mixes are best mixed with a mechanical drum mixer. This type of mixing is carried out outdoors, as it can be noisy and the materials used will cause high dust levels. *Regional variation: Belle mixer*

Industry term	Definition and regional variations
Dry lining	Lining masonry walls with plasterboards by directly bonding them with adhesive, known as 'dot and dab'. The term 'dry lining' comes from the plasterboards being a dry material as opposed to wet plaster.
Drying time	The time that needs to pass between applying a plaster coat or coats and being able to decorate.
Drywall driver	For driving in and extracting drywall screws. They come with various voltages including 110V, but 14.4V or 18V are probably the most practical. These drivers can either be battery-powered, so cordless, or powered by an electrical power cord.
Dubbing out	Filling out between uneven surfaces such as strong joints, building up the uneven surface until it is smooth.
Expanded metal lathing (EML)	Sheet material in the form of diamond-shaped mesh that is used to reinforce a surface. This material can be fixed with screws and plugs, galvanised nails or it can be bedded into the plaster material.
External angle	A reveal or return of a wall forming a right angle and a corner. The very tip of an external angle is called an arris. *See also* Internal angle.
Fat	The residue on a trowel created from trowelling up. This is dead plaster that should be discarded. If used to fill holes and misses it will not set properly – it will shrink and become soft and dusty.
Feather edge	A type of straight edge. Used for providing a firm and straight guide against which to cut. *See also* Straight edge.

Industry term	Definition and regional variations
Firstings and seconds 	Two gauges of plaster used to cast moulds. The 'firstings' is the first application of plaster. Its purpose is to prevent reinforcing materials from penetrating and showing through the face of the cast. The 'seconds' is the second mix which will have hessian and laths incorporated during the casting process. This makes the cast stronger, meaning you can use less plaster and therefore the cast is lighter.
Flash set	Where gypsum plaster sets far more quickly than expected. Can be caused by using dirty or contaminated water, tools and equipment, or out-of-date or poorly stored plaster.
Flat brush 	For applying clean water when trowelling up.
Flat workbenches 	Flat workbenches are essential for making moulding work. Modern benches are made from a sturdy steel frame and a thick plywood top that needs to be sealed with shellac. Traditional benches were built with brick or blocks and contained a solid plaster top bench that was costly and time consuming to construct. *Regional variation: plasterer's bench*
Float 	Used to consolidate the screed, as well as to provide a finish. These tools are generally made from polyurethane.
Floor scraper 	A floor scraper is often used with a sweeping brush for cleaning the work area during and after working.
Foundation 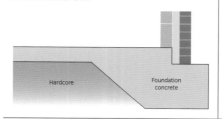	Used to spread the load of a building to the sub-soil.

Industry term	Definition and regional variations
Galvanised nail	When a protective zinc coating has been applied to steel nails to prevent corrosion or rusting which could cause unsightly staining on the finished plasterboard or cause the fixing to fail.
Gauging materials	The technical term for measuring materials, in particular the materials used in a plaster mix.
Gauging trowel	When mixing is in progress, this tool can be used to clean the rim of the mixing bucket, moving dry unmixed plaster back to the centre of the bucket. It is also used for cleaning and removing excess material off the straight edge and to clean plaster droppings by scraping the floor. *Regional variation: bull nosed trowel*
Gaul	A hollow or miss on the surface of the finished plaster. It needs to be filled with fresh plaster for a neat finish.
Green	Where plaster has set but not fully hardened. If you were to press a thumb into it you would not leave a dent, but if you were to drag your nail across it you would leave a scratch.
Hard hand brush	This type of brush is used for cleaning tools and equipment. It has harder bristles than a standard brush and will not wear down as quickly.
Hawk	Used to hold and transfer a workable amount of plaster from the spot board to the wall. The hawk is used in conjunction with the trowel to manipulate and apply the plaster directly onto the background surface. Hawks were traditionally made from timber, but modern ones are made from polyurethane or aluminium. *Regional variation: hand board*
Health and Safety Executive (HSE)	The national independent watchdog for work-related health, safety and illness. It works to reduce work-related death and serious injury in workplaces throughout Great Britain.

Industry term	Definition and regional variations
Heel 	The back of a laying on trowel's blade. *See also* Toe.
Hemihydrate	Where a substance's natural water content has been reduced by 50–75%.
Hop-up 	Purpose-made access equipment made of aluminium or timber that allow you to work up to standard ceiling heights. Their design allows you to step onto a platform from the ground without stretching.
Housekeeping 	Making sure that your work area is kept safe and tidy.
Industrial Standards	Minimum standards of quality of completed work universally adopted within the industry.
Internal angle 	A corner that you can put things in. *See also* External angle.
Internal angle trowel 	For finishing internal angles. *Regional variation: corner trowel*
Joint rule 	The joint rule has various uses in moulding work. Joint rules are flat blades and can be used for forming mitre joints. Another use is to form and align fibrous casts during fixing. Old joint rules can be used to scrape clean benches during and after the casting process, removing plaster droppings and splashes. *Regional variation: scraper*

Industry term	Definition and regional variations
Key	How rough or smooth a background surface is. Creating a rough surface, such as when using a comb scratcher, on a background helps the plaster adhere to it.
Kicking out	Where plaster forms a thicker ridge along the bottom of a wall. This makes it difficult for skirting boards to be fitted as they cannot sit flush to the wall.
Kinetic lifting	A method of lifting that ensures the risk of injury is reduced.
Laitance	A layer of weak material that comes to the top of concrete as it sets.
Large bristled brush	A large bristled brush has many uses, such as cleaning tools and equipment, or applying water or slurries to backgrounds. *Regional variation: hand brush*
Lath hammer	A traditional tool used by plasterers, before plasterboard was widely used, to cut wooden laths when lathing. Also used for hacking off old sand–lime plaster from walls and for hammering in plasterboard nails. *Regional variation: drywall hammer*
Lump hammer	Lump hammers are made with timber, steel or fibreglass shafts (handles) that are inserted into a rectangular head with a flat face made from cast iron. Its purpose, like any hammer, is to cause impact, knocking against the head of the bolster to remove old plaster from backgrounds. *Regional variation: club hammer*
Manufacturer's instructions	Manufacturer's instructions say what a product may be used for, how it is to be installed and what conditions it can be exposed to.

Industry term	Definition and regional variations
Mechanical breaker 	A breaker is a heavy-duty power tool generally used on hard, stubborn areas of plaster that are difficult to remove by hand using just a hammer and bolster. Mechanical breakers are very heavy and noisy when in use.
Method statement	A description of the intended method of carrying out a task, often linked to a risk assessment.
Mixing stand 	This is an essential piece of equipment to keep the mixing tool off the ground, preventing it from picking up dirt and contaminating the mix. This will also prevent trailing leads which can cause trip hazards.
Mortar (traditional) 	Coarse sand, hydraulic lime and horse or goat hair are the materials used for making traditional mortar. It is best mixed in a portable or small pan mixer.
Nodules 	Small balls of plaster left behind on the surface after devil floating. They are created from the plaster dragged out of the grooves by the nails of the devil float when forming the key. *Regional variation: snots*
Ordinary Portland Cement (OPC) 	A type of cement used in mixes. It is used with PVA to become a slurry and strong bonding agent for cement-based plasters. It is also a binder when used in screeds. It has an initial setting time of no less than 45 minutes and a final set of no more than 10 hours.
Pad saw 	A saw 6–8 inches long, used for cutting out holes in plasterboards for electrical sockets and pipework, etc. Also used when making complex cuts.

Industry term	Definition and regional variations
Pan mixer 	Equipment used to mix materials on site. The pan mixer has a large pan with two steel wheels that rotate around a central column in the pan. The materials are placed in the pan and the rotary action of the wheel forces the materials together. When the mix is ready, a gate in the base of the pan is opened and the mix is pushed through the gate.
Perimeter 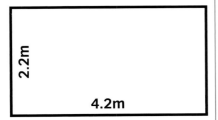	The distance around an object or room.
Perlite 	A lightweight aggregate used in pre-mixed plastering materials. It is a naturally occurring mineral that is mined, then crushed and heated.
Personal protective equipment (PPE) 	This is defined in the Regulations as 'all equipment (including clothing affording protection against the weather) which is intended to be worn or held by a person at work and which protects against one or more risks to a person's health or safety.' For example, safety helmets, gloves, eye protection, high-visibility clothing, safety foot-wear and safety harnesses.
Plastering trowel 	The majority of plastering trowels are made from stainless steel and come in various sizes, 'pre-worn', and with different handle materials. There are various types and makes of trowels used in our industry today.
Plated drywall screw 	A screw that has a rust-resistant zinc coating or black phosphate coating. They are sharp pointed and can be used to fix plasterboard to timber or steel channels.
Plunger 	A traditional mixing tool used to mix the plaster when added to water. During and after the mixing process it should be kept off the floor to prevent any bits of debris from sticking to the bottom of the tool, which could contaminate the next mix. *Regional variation: plasterer's mixing wheel*

Industry term	Definition and regional variations
Pointing hammer	This hammer has a flat end on one side and a pointed end on the other. It is a good tool for getting in between thin, tight surfaces like brick and stone to rake out the joints.
Pre-cast plasterwork	Moulds that have been cast in a workshop before fixing.
Pre-mixed plaster	Plaster materials that have been mixed in a processing plant and are sold bagged, needing only clean water added for mixing. Modern pre-mixed plasters are a mixture of gypsum and lightweight aggregates (vermiculite and perlite).
Price work	Where the amount you are paid depends on the amount of work you complete.
Pricing for work	Calculating and costing for plastering work.
Profile	The shape and pattern of the mould outline. The desired profile is normally outlined in the working drawing, unless you are matching an existing pattern from an original.
Prohibition notice	Issued by an HSE or local authority inspector when there is an immediate risk of personal injury. Receiving one means you are breaking health and safety regulations.
PVA	PVA is the abbreviation for polyvinyl acetate, a water-based glue that is used for preparing background surfaces by improving adhesion.
Ratio	The proportion of materials that are mixed together, eg six parts sand to one part cement.

Industry term	Definition and regional variations
Release agent	A substance applied to the surface of a mould to ease its removal after the plaster has set.
Retarder	A chemical additive that slows down the setting time of gypsum plasters, casting plaster, and cement.
Reverse mould Plaster reverse mould	A mould that is the 'back to front' version of the shape or pattern that you want to produce. There are four processes that can be used for making reverse moulds: plaster, rubber and fibreglass reverse moulds, and positive moulds.
Risk assessment	An assessment of the hazards and risks associated with an activity and the reduction and monitoring of them.
Rotary kiln	A large kiln that is set at an angle. The heat source is at the bottom of the kiln so it is cooler towards the top. As the whole kiln rotates, the limestone and clay mixture inside travels through it.
Rubber bowls	Plaster for fibrous plastering is generally mixed by hand in flexible rubber bowls that are easy to clean after use. *Regional variation: mixing bowl*
Sand	Sand is an aggregate used to bulk a plastering mix. Well-graded sand will have small, medium and large grains that are angular in shape. There are several types of sand: dredged, pit and coarse/crushed aggregate.
Scabbling	The removal of the surface finish by mechanical means, producing a suitable key.

Industry term	Definition and regional variations
Scale	The ratio of the size on a drawing to the size of the real thing that it represents. It is impossible to fit a full-sized drawing of a building onto a sheet of paper, so it is necessary to scale the size of the building to enable it to fit. Scale rules are used to draw scaled-down buildings on paper.
Scarifier	Like a comb scratcher, this is used to form a key on scratch coats. A scarifier is preferred on lightweight plaster surfaces. It has more teeth than a comb scratcher.
Screed rail	Used to help keep the floor flat.
Scrim	Scrim is an open-weave material that comes in rolls from 50–100mm wide and can be stuck over all joints in plasterboard walls and ceilings. It can even be stuck over joints where they meet other walls, such as around the perimeter of the ceiling.
Scrimming up	Applying scrim to reinforce the joints when fixing plasterboards.
Scutch hammer	This hammer has sharp teeth and can be used for removing plaster. It leaves a rough surface on backgrounds. *Regional variation: scutching hammer*

Industry term	Definition and regional variations
Services 	Those provided by utility companies, eg gas, electricity and water.
Setting time 	The time between mixing cement or gypsum plaster with water and the mixture starting to harden.
Shank 	The part of a trowel that spreads out from the handle along the back of the flat face, attaching them together.
Shelf life	The use by date of the product or material.
Shellac 	Liquid material applied with a brush to seal porous surfaces and form a protective skin in fibrous plasterwork.
Silt	Fine grains of sand. Too much silt in a plastering mix will prevent the cement from binding with the sand and cause the mix to be weak.
Slurry 	A thin, sloppy cement applied to backgrounds in order to bond plaster to its surface.

Industry term	Definition and regional variations
Small brushes 	Used to clean detail work and sometimes used to apply wet plaster into the recess and joins of moulds where a small tool does not reach.
Small tools leaf and square 	Used for minor moulding detail work. Also used for filling in joints in fibrous work.
Spatula 	To aid flattening and finishing of one coat plaster.
Specification 	A contract document that contains information on mix ratios and required standards of workmanship. This document will tell you how much of each material should be added to make the required mix.
Spirit level 	Used to ensure a level surface, ie when checking a wall is plumb.
Spot board and stand 	These are used to hold the plaster mix. A good spot board should be made from 18mm thick plywood that will not warp or bend. The spot board stand is made from steel and will normally have four legs to take the weight of the spot board at each corner when loaded with the mix. Spot board stands are designed to be erected and dismantled with ease, so they take up less space when not in use. They should be set out as close as possible to the wall in order to reduce the need to transfer the material over long distances.

Industry term	Definition and regional variations
Square	For setting floor screeds at the datum level.
Square edge plasterboard	Plasterboard that has its edges cut at a 90° angle from its face. *See also* Tapered edge plasterboard.
Staggered	Refers to the joint arrangement of plasterboards when they are fixed in place to timber or steel channel backgrounds – the vertical edges should not form a straight line.
Staple gun	Used for fixing beads to plasterboard.
Stock rotation	Making sure that older materials (such as bags of plaster) are at the front and/or top of the stack and so are used first, before their use by date.
Straight edge	Made from aluminium, this tool has many uses. Its main use will be to rule plaster surfaces and check for straightness. Another use is to form angles or the edges of returns and reveals before fitting them with standard angle beads. *See also* Feather edge.
Strike off	The built-up plaster area on the back of a cast which will come into contact with the background surface when fitted in place.

Industry term	Definition and regional variations
Stud walling/studwork 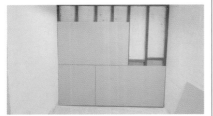	A partition wall constructed from lengths of timber that make a frame to fix sheet materials to.
Substrate	A stable background onto which other materials can be applied.
Suction 	The rate at which a background absorbs moisture. No suction or low suction indicates that the background is hard or dense. High-suction backgrounds will absorb moisture from the plaster mix and may cause it to dry too quickly when applied.
Surform 	Used for smoothing off cut edges or trimming down boards that are slightly too long. Curved cuts can also be formed using this tool. *Regional variations: rasp, plasterboard plane*
Sweeping brush 	*See* Floor scraper.
Symbols 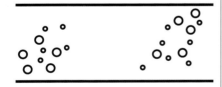 Concrete	Used on drawings to indicate different types of building materials.
Tape measure 	For measuring accurately, particularly when cutting plasterboard. To prevent confusion and mistakes, use tape measures with metric-only scales.

Industry term	Definition and regional variations
Tapered edge plasterboard 	Plasterboard that has its edges cut at a slant. *See also* Square cut plasterboard.
Tender	To submit a cost or price for work in an attempt to win the contract to do the work.
Three coat work	Also known as 'scratch, float and set' in internal plastering, this is three distinct layers of plaster. The first coat – the render or scratch – evens out an uneven background. The second coat – the float – provides a true flat surface for the third coat, which is called the set or finish.
Tin snips	Used to cut EML and beading, and to cut zinc/aluminium templates when constructing a running mould.
Toe	The front of a laying on trowel's blade. *See also* Heel.
Tool bag	A plasterer's tool bag contains many items that will need to be maintained and cleaned after use. It can be used to store the tools safely and securely, helping to keep them damage free and prolonging their life. *Regional variations: tool kit, holdall*
Trowelling up	The final procedure in the finishing process when a smooth texture is achieved.
Unbound edge	The short edge of a plasterboard sheet where the core is visible. *See also* Bound edge.

Industry term	Definition and regional variations
Undercut moulding members 	A model or mould with overhang patterns. They can be difficult to remove when cast unless the reverse mould is made from flexible material.
Vermiculite 	Like perlite, vermiculite is a naturally occurring mineral that is mined, then crushed and heated. It is a lightweight aggregate added to pre-mixed lightweight plaster to improve its bonding capabilities.
Wall plates 	Timber that runs along the top of a wall, to which the roof is fixed. When timber wall plates need to be plastered, using EML is a good way of reinforcing the timber and providing a key.
Water level 	For setting a datum line, particularly in floor screeding.
Wire brush 	This is a good tool for cleaning the face of backgrounds that still contain old dry plaster or flaking paint.
Wire brush attachment 	This can be fitted to a power drill to remove paint and expose the background surface.
Wooden laths 	Thin strips of wood 1.5m long, 30mm wide and 6mm thick that were traditionally fixed to studwork and ceilings. They were used before the widespread use of plasterboards and EML to form a background for plasterwork.
Work schedule	A series of events where the order of activities and the amount of time involved has been planned out. This is usually shown in the form of a bar or Gantt chart. *Regional variation: programme of work, labour schedule*

Chapter 1
Unit 201: Health, safety and welfare in construction

A career in the building industry can be a very rewarding one, both personally and financially. However, building sites and workshops are potentially very dangerous places; there are many potential hazards in the construction industry. Many construction operatives (workers) are injured each year, some fatally. Regulations have been brought in over the years to reduce accidents and improve working conditions.

By reading this chapter you will know about:

1 The health and safety regulations, roles and responsibilities.
2 Accident and emergency reporting procedures and documentation.
3 Identifying hazards in the workplace.
4 Health and welfare in the workplace.
5 Handling materials and equipment safely.
6 Access equipment and working at heights.
7 Working with electrical equipment in the workplace.
8 Using personal protective equipment (PPE).
9 The cause of fire and fire emergency procedures.

HEALTH AND SAFETY LEGISLATION

According to the Health and Safety Executive (HSE) figures, in 2011/12:

- Forty-nine construction operatives were fatally injured. Twenty-three of these operatives were self-employed. This compares with an average of 59 fatalities over the previous five years, of which an average of 19 fatally injured construction operatives were self-employed.

- The rate of fatal injury per 100,000 construction operatives was 2.3, compared with a five-year average of 2.5.

- Construction industry operatives were involved in 28% of fatal injuries across all industry sectors and it accounts for the greatest number of fatal injuries in any industry sector.

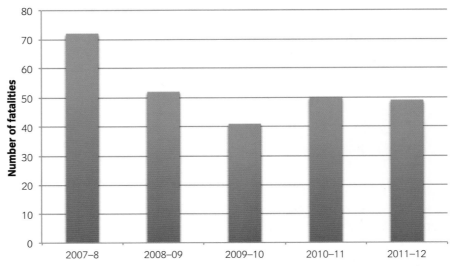

Number and rate of fatal injuries to workers in construction (RIDDOR)

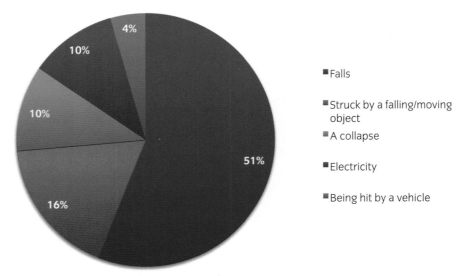

Proportion of fatalities in 2011/12 in construction

Health and safety legislation and great efforts made by the industry have made workplaces much safer in recent years. It is the responsibility of everyone involved in the building industry to continue to make it safer. Statistics are not just meaningless numbers – they represent injuries to real people. Many people believe that an accident will never happen to them, but it can. Accidents can:

- have a devastating effect on lives and families

- cost a lot financially in injury claims

- result in prosecution

- lead to job loss if an employee broke their company's safety policy.

Employers have an additional duty to ensure operatives have access to welfare facilities, eg drinking water, first aid and toilets, which will be discussed later in this chapter.

If everyone who works in the building industry pays close attention to health, safety and welfare, all operatives – including you – have every chance of enjoying a long, injury-free career.

UK HEALTH AND SAFETY REGULATIONS, ROLES AND RESPONSIBILITIES

Standard construction safety equipment

In the UK there are many laws (legislation) that have been put into place to make sure that those working on construction sites, and members of the public, are kept healthy and safe. If these laws and regulations are not obeyed then prosecutions can take place. Worse still, there is a greater risk of injury and damage to your health and the health of those around you.

The principal legislation that relates to health, safety and welfare in construction is:

- Health and Safety at Work Act (HASAWA) 1974

- Control of Substances Hazardous to Health (COSHH) Regulations 2002

- Reporting of Injuries, Diseases and Dangerous Occurrences Regulations (RIDDOR) 2013

- Construction, Design and Management (CDM) Regulations 2007

- Provision and Use of Work Equipment Regulations (PUWER) 1998

- Manual Handling Operations Regulations 1992

- Personal Protective Equipment (PPE) at Work Regulations 1992

- Work at Height Regulations 2005 (as amended)
- Lifting Operations and Lifting Equipment Regulations (LOLER) 1998
- Control of Noise at Work Regulations 2005
- Control of Vibration at Work Regulations 2005.

HEALTH AND SAFETY AT WORK ACT (HASAWA) 1974

The Health and Safety at Work Act (HASAWA) 1974 applies to all workplaces. Everyone who works on a building site or in a workshop is covered by this legislation. This includes employed and self-employed operatives, subcontractors, the employer and those delivering goods to the site. It not only protects those working, it also ensures the safety of anyone else who might be nearby.

KEY EMPLOYER RESPONSIBILITIES

The key employer health and safety responsibilities under HASAWA are to:

- provide a safe working environment
- provide safe access (entrance) and egress (exit) to the work area
- provide adequate staff training
- have a written health and safety policy in place
- provide health and safety information and display the appropriate signs
- carry out risk assessments
- provide safe machinery and equipment and to ensure it is well-maintained and in a safe condition
- provide adequate supervision to ensure safe practices are carried out
- involve trade union safety representatives, where appointed, in matters relating to health and safety
- provide personal protective equipment (**PPE**) free of charge, ensure the appropriate PPE is used whenever needed, and that operatives are properly supervised
- ensure materials and substances are transported, used and stored safely.

PPE

This is defined in the Personal Protective Equipment at Work Regulations 1992 as 'all equipment (including clothing affording protection against the weather) which is intended to be worn or held by a person at work and which protects against one or more risks to a person's health or safety.'

Risk assessments and method statements

The HASAWA requires that employers must carry out regular **risk assessments** to make sure that there are minimal dangers to their employees in a workplace.

Risk assessment

An assessment of the hazards and risks associated with an activity and the reduction and monitoring of them

Risk Assessment

Activity / Workplace assessed: Return to work after accident
Persons consulted / involved in risk assessment
Date:
Reviewed on:

Location:
Risk assessment reference number:
Review date:
Review by:

Significant hazard	People at risk and what is the risk Describe the harm that is likely to result from the hazard (eg cut, broken leg, chemical burn etc) and who could be harmed (eg employees, contractors, visitors etc)	Existing control measure What is currently in place to control the risk?	Risk rating Use matrix identified in guidance note Likelihood (L) Severity (S) Multiply (L) * (S) to produce risk rating (RR)				Further action required What is required to bring the risk down to an acceptable level? Use hierarchy of control described in guidance note when considering the controls needed	Actioned to: Who will complete the action?	Due date: When will the action be completed by?	Completion date: Initial and date once the action has been completed
			L	S	RR	L/M/H				
Uneven floors	Operatives	Verbal warning and supervision	2	1	2	m	None applicable	Site supervisor	Active now	Ongoing
Steps	Operatives	Verbal warning	2	1	2	m	None applicable	Site supervisor	Active now	Ongoing
Staircases	Operatives	Verbal warning	2	2	4	m	None applicable	Site supervisor	Active now	Ongoing

	Likelihood			
		1 **Unlikely**	**2** **Possible**	**3** **Very likely**
Severity	**1** Slight/minor injuries/minor damage	1	2	3
	2 Medium injuries/significant damage	2	4	6
	3 Major injury/extensive damage	3	6	9

Likelihood
3 – Very likely
2 – Possible
1 – Unlikely

Severity
3 – Major injury/extensive damage
2 – Medium injury/significant damage
1 – Slight/minor damage

1   – Low risk, action should be taken to reduce the risk if reasonably practicable
2, 3, 4 – Medium risk, is a significant risk and would require an appropriate level of resource
6 & 9 – High risk, may require considerable resources to mitigate. Control should focus on elimination of risk, if not possible control should be obtained by following the hierarchy of control

123 type risk assessment

A risk assessment is a legally required tool used by employers to:

- identify work hazards
- assess the risk of harm arising from these hazards
- adequately control the risk.

Risk assessments are carried out as follows:

1 Identify the hazards. Consider the environment in which the job will be done. Which tools and materials will be used?

2 Identify who might be at risk. Think about operatives, visitors and members of the public.

3   Evaluate the risk. How severe is the potential injury? How likely is it to happen? A severe injury may be possible but may also be very improbable. On the other hand a minor injury might be very likely.

4   If there is an unacceptable risk, can the job be changed? Could different tools or materials be used instead?

5   If the risk is acceptable, what measures can be taken to reduce the risk? This could be training, special equipment and using PPE.

6   Keep good records. Explain the findings of the risk assessment to the operatives involved. Update the risk assessment as required – there may be new machinery, materials or staff. Even adverse weather can bring additional risks.

A **method statement** is required by law and is a useful way of recording the hazards involved in a specific task. It is used to communicate the risk and precautions required to all those involved in the work. It should be clear, uncomplicated and easy to understand as it is for the benefit of those carrying out the work (and their immediate supervisors).

Inductions and tool box talks

Any new visitors to and operatives on a site will be given an induction. This will explain:

- the layout of the site

- any hazards of which they need to be aware

- the location of welfare facilities

- the assembly areas in case of emergency

- site rules.

Tool box talks are short talks given at regular intervals. They give timely safety reminders and outline any new hazards that may have arisen because construction sites change as they develop. Weather conditions such as extreme heat, wind or rain may create new hazards.

KEY EMPLOYEE RESPONSIBILITIES

The HASAWA covers the responsibilities of employees and subcontractors:

- You must work in a safe manner and take care at all times.

- You must make sure you do not put yourself or others at risk by your actions or inactions.

Method statement

A description of the intended method of carrying out a task, often linked to a risk assessment

INDUSTRY TIP

The Construction Skills Certification Scheme (CSCS) was set up in the mid-'90s with the aim of improving site operatives' competence to reduce accidents and drive up on-site efficiency. Card holders must take a health and safety test. The colour of card depends on level of qualification held and job role. For more information see www.cscs.uk.com

ACTIVITY

Think back to your induction. Write down what was discussed. Did you understand everything? Do you need any further information? If you have not had an induction, write a list of the things you think you need to know.

INDUSTRY TIP

Remember, if you are unsure about any health and safety issue always seek help and advice.

- You must co-operate with your employer in regard to health and safety. If you do not you risk injury (to yourself or others), prosecution, a fine and loss of employment. Do not take part in practical jokes and horseplay.

- You must use any equipment and safeguards provided by your employer. For example, you must wear, look after and report any damage to the PPE that your employer provides.

- You must not interfere or tamper with any safety equipment.

- You must not misuse or interfere with anything that is provided for employees' safety.

FIRST AID AND FIRST-AID KITS

First aid should only be applied by someone trained in first aid. Even a minor injury could become infected and therefore should be cleaned and a dressing applied. If any cut or injury shows signs of infection, becomes inflamed or painful seek medical attention. An employer's first-aid needs should be assessed to indicate whether a first-aider (someone trained in first aid) is necessary. The minimum requirement is to appoint a person to take charge of first-aid arrangements. The role of this appointed person includes looking after the first-aid equipment and facilities and calling the emergency services when required.

First-aid kits vary according to the size of the workforce. First-aid boxes should not contain tablets or medicines.

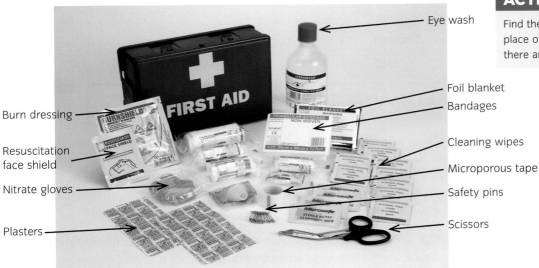

First-aid kit

INDUSTRY TIP

The key employee health and safety responsibilities are to:
- work safely
- work in partnership with your employer
- report hazards and accidents as per company policy.

INDUSTRY TIP

Employees must not be charged for anything given to them or done for them by the employer in relation to safety.

INDUSTRY TIP

In the event of an accident, first aid will be carried out by a qualified first aider. First aid is designed to stabilise a patient for later treatment if required. The casualty may be taken to hospital or an ambulance may be called. In the event of an emergency you should raise the alarm.

ACTIVITY

Your place of work or training will have an appointed first-aider who deals with first aid. Find out who they are and how to make contact with them.

ACTIVITY

Find the first-aid kit in your workplace or place of training. What is inside it? Is there anything missing?

SOURCES OF HEALTH AND SAFETY INFORMATION

Source	How they can help
Health and Safety Executive (HSE)	A government body that oversees health and safety in the workplace. It produces health and safety literature such as the **Approved Code of Practice** (ACoP).
Construction Skills	The construction industry training body produces literature and is directly involved with construction training.
The Royal Society for the Prevention of Accidents (ROSPA)	It produces literature and gives advice.
The Royal Society for Public Health	An independent, multi-disciplinary charity that is dedicated to the promotion and protection of collective human health and wellbeing.
Institution of Occupational Safety and Health (IOSH)	A chartered body for health and safety practitioners. The world's largest health and safety professional membership organisation.
The British Safety Council	It helps businesses with their health, safety and environmental management.

HEALTH AND SAFETY EXECUTIVE (HSE)

The HSE is a body set up by the government. The HSE ensures that the law is carried out correctly and has extensive powers to ensure that it can do its job. It can make spot checks in the workplace, bring the police, examine anything on the premises and take things away to be examined.

If the HSE finds a health and safety problem that breaks health and safety law it might issue an **improvement notice** giving the employer a set amount of time to correct the problem. For serious health and safety risks where there is a risk of immediate major injury, it can issue a **prohibition notice** which will stop all work on site until the health and safety issues are rectified. It may take an employer, employee, self-employed person (subcontractor) or anyone else involved with the building process to court for breaking health and safety legislation.

Approved Code of Practice

ACoP gives practical advice for those in the construction industry in relation to using machinery

INDUSTRY TIP

There are many other trade organisations, eg the Timber Research and Development Association (TRADA), which also offer advice on safe practices.

ACTIVITY

You have been asked to give a tool box talk because of several minor injuries involving tripping on site. What topics would you include in this talk?

INDUSTRY TIP

To find out more information on the sources in the table, enter their names into a search engine on the internet.

Improvement notice

Issued by an HSE or local authority inspector to formally notify a company that improvements are needed to the way it is working

Prohibition notice

Issued by an HSE or local authority inspector when there is an immediate risk of personal injury. They are not issued lightly and if you are on the receiving end of one, you are clearly breaking a health and safety regulation

The HSE provides a lot of advice on safety and publishes numerous booklets and information sheets. One example of this is the Approved Code of Practice (ACoP) which applies to wood working machinery. The ACoP has a special legal status and employers and employees are expected to work within its guidelines.

The duties of the HSE are to:

- give advice

- issue improvement and prohibition notices

- caution

- prosecute

- investigate.

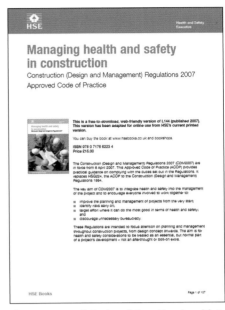

The Approved Code of Practice booklet is available free online

CONTROL OF SUBSTANCES HAZARDOUS TO HEALTH (COSHH) REGULATIONS 2002

The Control of Substances Hazardous to Health (COSHH) Regulations 2002 control the use of dangerous substances, eg preservatives, fuels, solvents, adhesives, cement and oil based paint. These have to be moved, stored and used safely without polluting the environment. It also covers hazardous substances produced while working, eg wood dust produced when sanding or drilling.

Hazardous substances may be discovered during the building process, eg lead-based paint or asbestos. These are covered by separate regulations.

When considering substances and materials that may be hazardous to health an employer should do the following to comply with COSHH:

- Read and check the COSHH safety data sheet that comes with the product. It will outline any hazards associated with the product and the safety measures to be taken.

- Check with the supplier if there are any known risks to health.

- Use the trade press to find out if there is any information about this substance or material.

- Use the HSE website, or other websites, to check any known issues with the substance or material.

When assessing the risk of a potentially dangerous substance or material it is important to consider how operatives could be exposed to it. For example:

Example of COSHH data sheet

- by breathing in gas or mist

- by swallowing it

- by getting it into their eyes

- through their skin, either by contact or through cuts.

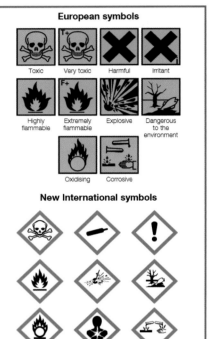

Safety data sheets

Products you use may be 'dangerous for supply'. If so, they will have a label that has one or more hazard symbols. Some examples are given here.

These products include common substances in everyday use such as paint, bleach, solvent or fillers. When a product is 'dangerous for supply', by law, the supplier must provide you with a safety data sheet. Note: medicines, pesticides and cosmetic products have different legislation and don't have a safety data sheet. Ask the supplier how the product can be used safely.

Safety data sheets can be hard to understand, with little information on measures for control. However, to find out about health risks and emergency situations, concentrate on:

- Sections 2 and 16 of the sheet, which tell you what the dangers are;
- Sections 4-8, which tell you about emergencies, storage and handling.

Since 2009, new international symbols have been gradually replacing the European symbols. Some of them are similar to the European symbols, but there is no single word describing the hazard. Read the hazard statement on the packaging and the safety data sheet from the supplier.

Hazard checklist

☐ Does any product you use have a danger label?
☐ Does your process produce gas, fume, dust, mist or vapour?
☐ Is the substance harmful to breathe in?
☐ Can the substance harm your skin?
☐ Is it likely that harm could arise because of the way you use or produce it?
☐ What are you going to do about it?
   - Use something else?
   - Use it in another, safer way?
   - Control it to stop harm being caused?

CONTROL MEASURES

The control measures below are in order of importance.

1 Eliminate the use of the harmful substance and use a safer one. For instance, swap high **VOC** oil based paint for a lower VOC water-borne paint.

2 Use a safer form of the product. Is the product available ready mixed? Is there a lower strength option that will still do the job?

VOC

The measurement of volatile organic compounds shows how much pollution a product will emit into the air when in use

INDUSTRY TIP

Product data sheets are free and have to be produced by the supplier of the product.

3 Change the work method to emit less of the substance. For instance, applying paint with a brush releases fewer VOCs into the air than spraying paint. Wet grinding produces less dust than dry grinding.

4 Enclose the work area so that the substance does not escape. This can mean setting up a tented area or closing doors.

5 Use extraction or filtration (eg a dust bag) in the work area.

6 Keep operatives in the area to a minimum.

7 Employers must provide appropriate PPE.

Paint with high VOC content

European symbols

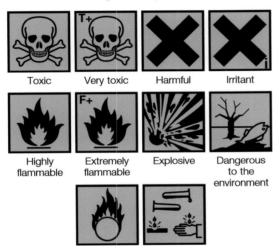

ACTIVITY

Think of three substances in your workplace or place of training that might be hazardous to health. Can you find a COSHH data sheet for each? (They can often be found on the internet if you search for the product.)

New International symbols

COSHH symbols. The international symbols will replace the European symbols in 2015

REPORTING OF INJURIES, DISEASES AND DANGEROUS OCCURRENCES REGULATIONS (RIDDOR) 2013

Despite all the efforts put into health and safety, incidents still happen. The Reporting of Injuries, Diseases and Dangerous Occurrences Regulations (RIDDOR) 2013 state that employers must report to the HSE all accidents that result in an employee needing more than seven days off work. Diseases and dangerous occurrences must also be reported. A serious occurrence that has not caused an injury (a near miss) should still be reported because next time it happens things might not work out as well.

Below are some examples of injuries, diseases and dangerous occurrences that would need to be reported:

- A joiner cuts off a finger while using a circular saw.
- A plumber takes a week off after a splinter in her hand becomes infected.
- A ground operative contracts **leptospirosis**.
- A labourer contracts dermatitis (a serious skin problem) after contact with an irritant substance.
- A scaffold suffers a collapse following severe weather, unauthorised alteration or overloading but no-one is injured.

Leptospirosis

Also known as Weil's disease, this is a serious disease spread by rats and cattle

The purpose of RIDDOR is to enable the HSE to investigate serious incidents and collate statistical data. This information is used to help reduce the number of similar accidents happening in future and to make the workplace safer.

INDUSTRY TIP

Accidents do not just affect the person who has the accident. Work colleagues or members of the public might be affected and so will the employer. The consequences may include:
- a poor company image (this may put off potential customers)
- loss of production
- insurance costs increasing
- closure of the site
- having to pay sick pay
- other additional costs.

New HSE guidelines require employers to pay an hourly rate for time taken by the HSE to investigate an accident. This is potentially very costly.

An F2508 injury report form

Although minor accidents and injuries are not reported to HSE, records must be kept. Accidents must be recorded in the accident book. This provides a record of what happened and is useful for future reference. Trends may become apparent and the employer may take action to try to prevent that particular type of accident occurring again.

CONSTRUCTION, DESIGN AND MANAGEMENT (CDM) REGULATIONS 2007

The Construction, Design and Management (CDM) Regulations 2007 focus attention on the effective planning and management of construction projects, from the design concept through to maintenance and repair. The aim is for health and safety considerations to be integrated into a project's development, rather than be an inconvenient afterthought. The CDM Regulations reduce the risk of harm to those that have to work on or use the structure throughout its life, from construction through to **demolition**.

CDM Regulations protect workers from the construction to demolition of large and complex structures

The CDM Regulations apply to all projects except for those arranged by private clients, ie work that isn't in furtherance of a business interest. Property developers need to follow the CDM Regulations.

Under the CDM Regulations, the HSE must be notified where the construction work will take:

■ more than 30 working days or

You have identified a potential risk. What action should you take? Make notes.

The CDM Regulations play a role in safety during demolition

Demolition

When something, often a building, is completely torn down and destroyed

- 500 working days in total, ie if 100 people work for 5 days (500 working days) the HSE will have to be notified.

DUTY HOLDERS

Under the CDM Regulations there are several duty holders, each with a specific role.

Duty holder	Role
Client	This is the person or organisation who wishes to have the work done. The client will check that: - all the team members are competent - the management is suitable - sufficient time is allowed for all stages of the project - welfare facilities are in place before construction starts. HSE notifiable projects require that the client appoints a CDM co-ordinator and principal contractor, and provides access to a health and safety file.
CDM co-ordinator	Appointed by the client, the co-ordinator advises and assists the client with CDM duties. The co-ordinator notifies the HSE before work starts. This role involves the co-ordination of the health and safety aspects of the design of the building and ensures good communication between the client, designers and contractors.
Designer	At the design stages the designer removes hazards and reduces risks. The designer provides information about the risks that cannot be eliminated. Notifiable projects require that the designer checks that the client is aware of their CDM duties and that a CDM co-ordinator has been appointed. The designer will also supply information for the health and safety file.
Principal contractor	The principal contractor will plan, manage and monitor the construction in liaison with any other involved contractors. This involves developing a written plan and site rules before the construction begins. The principal contractor ensures that the site is made secure and suitable welfare facilities are provided from the start and maintained throughout construction. The principal contractor will also make sure that all operatives have site inductions and any further training that might be required to make sure the workforce is competent.
Contractor	Subcontractors and self-employed operatives will plan, manage and monitor their own work and employees, co-operating with any main contractor in relation to site rules. Contractors will make sure that all operatives have any further training that might be required to make sure they are competent. A contractor also reports any incidents under RIDDOR to the principal contractor.
Operatives	Operatives need to check their own competence: Can you carry out the task you have been asked to do safely? Have you been trained to do this type of activity? Do you have the correct equipment to carry out this activity? You must follow all the site health and safety rules and procedures and fully co-operate with the rest of the team to ensure the health and safety of other operatives and others who may be affected by the work. Any health and safety issues must be reported.

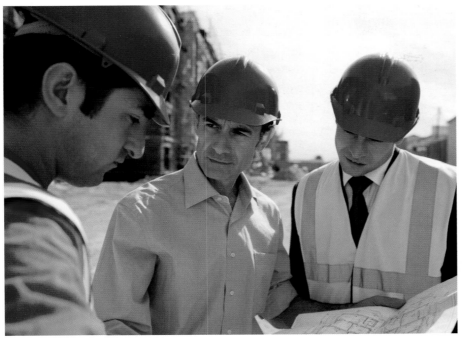

A client, a contractor and an operative looking over building plans ahead of construction

ACTIVITY

What would you do if you spotted any of these hazards?

WELFARE FACILITIES REQUIRED ON SITE UNDER THE CDM REGULATIONS

The table below shows the welfare facilities that must be available on site.

Facility	Site requirement
Sanitary conveniences (toilets) 	■ Suitable and sufficient toilets should be provided or made available. ■ Toilets should be adequately ventilated and lit and should be clean. ■ Separate toilet facilities should be provided for men and women.
Washing facilities 	■ Sufficient facilities must be available, and include showers if required by the nature of the work. ■ They should be in the same place as the toilets and near any changing rooms. ■ There must be a supply of clean hot (or warm) and cold running water, soap and towels. ■ There must be separate washing facilities provided for men and women unless the area is for washing hands and the face only.

Facility	Site requirement
Clean drinking water 	■ This must be provided or made available. ■ It should be clearly marked by an appropriate sign. ■ Cups should be provided unless the supply of drinking water is from a water fountain.
Changing rooms and lockers 	■ Changing rooms must be provided or made available if operatives have to wear special clothing and if they cannot be expected to change elsewhere. ■ There must be separate rooms for, or separate use of rooms by, men and women where necessary. ■ The rooms must have seating and include, where necessary, facilities to enable operatives to dry their special clothing and their own clothing and personal effects. ■ Lockers should also be provided.
Rest rooms or rest areas 	■ Rest rooms should have enough tables and seating with backs for the number of operatives likely to use them at any one time. ■ Where necessary, rest rooms should include suitable facilities for pregnant women or nursing mothers to rest lying down. ■ Arrangements must be made to ensure that meals can be prepared, heated and eaten. It must also be possible to boil water.

ACTIVITY

What facilities are provided at your workplace or place of training?

PROVISION AND USE OF WORK EQUIPMENT REGULATIONS (PUWER) 1998

The Provision and Use of Work Equipment Regulations (PUWER) 1998 place duties on:

■ people and companies who own, operate or have control over work equipment

■ employers whose employees use work equipment.

Work equipment can be defined as any machinery, appliance, apparatus, tool or installation for use at work (whether exclusively or not). This includes equipment that employees provide for their own use at work. The scope of work equipment is therefore extremely wide. The use of work equipment is also very widely interpreted and, according to the HSE, means 'any activity involving work equipment and includes starting, stopping, programming, setting, transporting, repairing, modifying, maintaining, servicing and cleaning.' It includes equipment such as diggers, electric planers, stepladders, hammers or wheelbarrows.

Under PUWER, work equipment must be:

- suitable for the intended use

- safe to use

- well maintained

- inspected regularly.

Regular inspection is important as a tool that was safe when it was new may no longer be safe after considerable use.

Additionally, work equipment must only be used by people who have received adequate instruction and training. Information regarding the use of the equipment must be given to the operator and must only be used for what it was designed to do.

Protective devices, eg emergency stops, must be used. Brakes must be fitted where appropriate to slow down moving parts to bring the equipment to a safe condition when turned off or stopped. Equipment must have adequate means of isolation. Warnings, either by signs or other means such as sounds or lights, must be used as appropriate. Access to dangerous parts of the machinery must be controlled. Some work equipment is subject to additional health and safety legislation which must also be followed.

Employers who use work equipment must manage the risks. ACoPs (see page 9) have been developed in line with PUWER. The ACoPs have a special legal status, as outlined in the introduction to the PUWER ACoP:

> *Following the guidance is not compulsory and you are free to take other action. But if you do follow the guidance you will normally be doing enough to comply with the law. Health and safety inspectors seek to secure compliance with the law and may refer to this guidance as illustrating good practice.*

INDUSTRY TIP

Abrasive wheels are used for grinding. Under PUWER these wheels can only be changed by someone who has received training to do this. Wrongly fitted wheels can explode!

ACTIVITY

All the tools you use for your work are covered by PUWER. They must be well maintained and suitable for the task. A damaged head on a bolster chisel must be reshaped. A split shaft on a joiner's wood chisel must be repaired. Why would these tools be dangerous in a damaged condition? List the reasons.

MANUAL HANDLING OPERATIONS REGULATIONS 1992

Employers must try to avoid manual handling within reason if there is a possibility of injury. If manual handling cannot be avoided then they must reduce the risk of injury by means of a risk assessment.

LIFTING AND HANDLING

Incorrect lifting and handling is a serious risk to your health. It is very easy to injure your back – just ask any experienced builder. An injured back can be very unpleasant, so it's best to look after it.

Here are a few things to consider when lifting:

- Assess the load. Is it too heavy? Do you need assistance or additional training? Is it an awkward shape?
- Can a lifting aid be used, such as any of the below?

An operative lifting heavy bricks

Wheelbarrow

Gin lift

Scissor lift

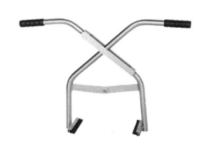

Kerb lifter

- Does the lift involve twisting or reaching?
- Where is the load going to end up? Is there a clear path? Is the place it's going to be taken to cleared and ready?

How to lift and place an item correctly

If you cannot use a machine, it is important that you keep the correct posture when lifting any load. The correct technique to do this is known as **kinetic lifting**. Always lift with your back straight, elbows in, knees bent and your feet slightly apart.

Kinetic lifting

A method of lifting that ensures that the risk of injury is reduced

Safe kinetic lifting technique

When placing the item, again be sure to use your knees and beware of trapping your fingers. If stacking materials, be sure that they are on a sound level base and on bearers if required.

Heavy objects that cannot easily be lifted by mechanical methods can be lifted by several people. It is important that one person in the team is in charge, and that lifting is done in a co-operative way. It has been known for one person to fall down and the others to then drop the item!

CONTROL OF NOISE AT WORK REGULATIONS 2005

Under the Control of Noise at Work Regulations 2005, duties are placed on employers and employees to reduce the risk of hearing damage to the lowest reasonable level practicable. Hearing loss caused by work is preventable. Hearing damage is permanent and cannot be restored once lost.

EMPLOYER'S DUTIES UNDER THE REGULATIONS

An employer's duties are:

- to carry out a risk assessment and identify who is at risk

- to eliminate or control its employees' exposure to noise at the workplace and to reduce the noise as far as practicable

- to provide suitable hearing protection

- to provide health surveillance to those identified as at risk by the risk assessment

- to provide information and training about the risks to their employees as identified by the risk assessment.

EMPLOYEES' DUTIES UNDER THE REGULATIONS

Employees must:

- make full and proper use of personal hearing protectors provided to them by their employer

- report to their employer any defect in any personal hearing protectors or other control measures as soon as is practicable.

NOISE LEVELS

Under the Regulations, specific actions are triggered at specific noise levels. Noise is measured in decibels and shown as dB(a). The two main action levels are 80dB(a) and 85dB(a).

Requirements at 80dB(a) to 85dB(a):

- Assess the risk to operatives' health and provide them with information and training.

- Provide suitable ear protection free of charge to those who request ear protection.

Requirements above 85dB(a):

- Reduce noise exposure as far as practicable by means other than ear protection.

- Set up an ear protection zone using suitable signage and segregation.

- Provide suitable ear protection free of charge to those affected and ensure they are worn.

PERSONAL PROTECTIVE EQUIPMENT (PPE) AT WORK REGULATIONS 1992

Employees and subcontractors must work in a safe manner. Not only must they wear the PPE that their employers provide but they must also look after it and report any damage to it. Importantly, employees must not be charged for anything given to them or done for them by the employer in relation to safety.

Ear defenders

Ear plugs

INDUSTRY TIP

The typical noise level for a hammer drill and a concrete mixer is 90 to 100dB(a).

ACTIVITY

Think about your place of work or training. What PPE do you think you should use when working with cement or using a powered planer?

The hearing and respiratory PPE provided for most work situations is not covered by these Regulations because other regulations apply to it. However, these items need to be compatible with any other PPE provided.

The main requirement of the Regulations is that PPE must be supplied and used at work wherever there are risks to health and safety that cannot be adequately controlled in other ways.

The Regulations also require that PPE is:

- included in the method statement

- properly assessed before use to ensure it is suitable

- maintained and stored properly

- provided to employees with instructions on how they can use it safely

- used correctly by employees.

An employer cannot ask for money from an employee for PPE, whether it is returnable or not. This includes agency workers if they are legally regarded as employees. If employment has been terminated and the employee keeps the PPE without the employer's permission, then, as long as it has been made clear in the contract of employment, the employer may be able to deduct the cost of the replacement from any wages owed.

Using PPE is a very important part of staying safe. For it to do its job properly it must be kept in good condition and used correctly. If any damage does occur to an article of PPE it is important that this is reported and it is replaced. It must also be remembered that PPE is a last line of defence and should not be used in place of a good safety policy!

ACTIVITY

Check the date on your safety helmet. Always update your safety helmet if it is out of date.

INDUSTRY TIP

Remember, you also have a duty of care for your own health.

A site safety sign showing the PPE required to work there

INDUSTRY TIP

You can get chemical burns from cement. Always wear gloves when working with cement.

The following table shows the type of PPE used in the workplace and explains why it is important to store, maintain and use PPE correctly. It also shows why it is important to check and report damage to PPE.

PPE	Correct use
Hard hat/safety helmet	Hard hats must be worn when there is danger of hitting your head or danger of falling objects. They often prevent a wide variety of head injuries. Most sites insist on hard hats being worn. They must be adjusted to fit your head correctly and must not be worn back to front! Check the date of manufacture as plastic can become brittle over time. Solvents, pens and paints can damage the plastic too.
Toe-cap boots or shoes Safety boots A nail in a construction worker's foot	Toe-cap boots or shoes are worn on most sites as a matter of course and protect the feet from heavy falling objects. Some safety footwear has additional insole protection to help prevent nails going up through the foot. Toe caps can be made of steel or lighter plastic.
Ear defenders and plugs Ear defenders Ear plugs	Your ears can be very easily damaged by loud noise. Ear protection will help prevent hearing loss while using loud tools or if there is a lot of noise going on around you. When using earplugs always ensure your hands are clean before handling the plugs as this reduces the risk of infection. If your ear defenders are damaged or fail to make a good seal around your ears have them replaced.
High-visibility (hi-viz) jacket	This makes it much easier for other people to see you. This is especially important when there is plant or vehicles moving in the vicinity.
Goggles and safety glasses   Safety goggles Safety glasses	These protect the eyes from dust and flying debris while you are working. It has been known for casualties to be taken to hospital after dust has blown up from a dry mud road. You only get one pair of eyes: look after them!

PPE	Correct use
Dust masks and respirators  Dust mask Respirator	Dust is produced during most construction work and it can be hazardous to your lungs. It can cause all sorts of ailments from asthma through to cancer. Wear a dust mask to filter this dust out. You must ensure it is well fitted. Another hazard is dangerous gases such as solvents. A respirator will filter out hazardous gases but a dust mask will not! Respirators are rated P1, P2 and P3, with P3 giving the highest protection.
Gloves   Latex glove Nitrile glove 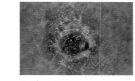 Gauntlet gloves Leather gloves	Gloves protect your hands. Hazards include cuts, abrasions, dermatitis, chemical burns or splinters. Latex and nitrile gloves are good for fine work, although some people are allergic to latex. Gauntlets provide protection from strong chemicals. Other types of gloves provide good grip and protect the fingers.  A chemical burn as a result of not wearing safety gloves
Sunscreen  Suncream Melanoma	Another risk, especially in the summer months, is sunburn. Although a good tan is sometimes considered desirable, over-exposure to the sun can cause skin cancer such as melanoma. When out in the sun, cover up and use sunscreen (ie suncream) on exposed areas of your body to prevent burning.
Preventing HAVS 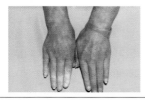	Hand–arm vibration syndrome (HAVS), also known as vibration white finger (VWF), is an industrial injury caused by using vibrating power tools (such as a hammer drill, vibrating poker and vibrating plate) for a long time. This injury is controlled by limiting the time such power tools are used. For more information see page 31.

ACTIVITY

You are working on a site and a brick falls on your head. Luckily, you are doing as you have been instructed and you are wearing a helmet. You notice that the helmet has a small crack in it. What do you do?

1 Carry on using it as your employer will charge you for a new one; after all it is only a small crack.
2 Take it to your supervisor as it will no longer offer you full protection and it will need replacing.
3 Buy a new helmet because the old one no longer looks very nice.

INDUSTRY TIP

The most important pieces of PPE when using a disc cutter are dust masks, glasses and ear protection.

WORK AT HEIGHT REGULATIONS 2005 (AS AMENDED)

The Work at Height Regulations 2005 (as amended) put several duties upon employers:

- Working at height should be avoided if possible.

- If working at height cannot be avoided, the work must be properly organised with risk assessments carried out.

- Risk assessments should be regularly updated.

- Those working at height must be trained and competent.

- A method statement must be provided.

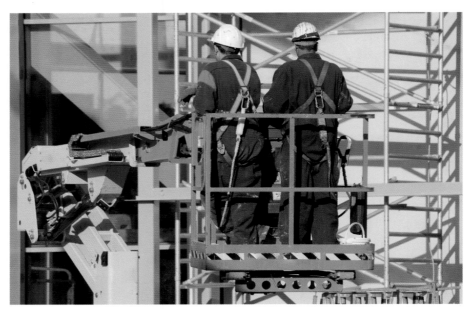
Workers wearing safety harnesses on an aerial access platform

Several points should be considered when working at height:

- How long is the job expected to take?

- What type of work will it be? It could be anything from fitting a single light bulb, through to removing a chimney or installing a roof.
  - How is the access platform going to be reached? By how many people?
  - Will people be able to get on and off the structure safely? Could there be overcrowding?

- What are the risks to passers-by? Could debris or dust blow off and injure anyone on the road below?

- What are the conditions like? Extreme weather, unstable buildings and poor ground conditions need to be taken into account.

A cherry picker can assist you when working at height

ACCESS EQUIPMENT AND SAFE METHODS OF USE

The means of access should only be chosen after a risk assessment has been carried out. There are various types of access.

Ladders

Ladders are normally used for access onto an access platform. They are not designed for working from except for light, short-duration work. A ladder should lean at an angle of 75°, ie one unit out for every four units up.

Strong upper resting point

Adequate lap on extension ladders

Ground back slope not exceeding 6°

Ground side slope not exceeding 16°, clean and free of slippery algae and moss

Using a ladder correctly

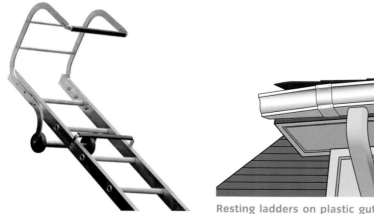

Roof ladder

Resting ladders on plastic guttering can cause it to bend and break

The following images show how to use a ladder or stepladder safely.

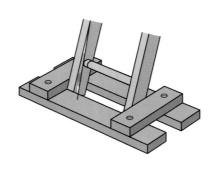

A ladder secured at the base.

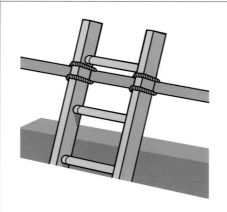

A ladder secured at the top of a platform for working from.

Access ladders should extend 1m above the landing point to provide a strong handhold.

Certain stepladders are unsafe to work from the top three rungs.

Don't overreach, and stay on the same rung.

Grip the ladder when climbing and remember to keep three points of contact.

INDUSTRY TIP

Always complete ladder pre-checks. Check the stiles (the two uprights) and rungs for damage such as splits or cracks. Do not use painted ladders because the paint could be hiding damage! Check all of the equipment including any stays and feet.

Stepladders

Stepladders are designed for light, short-term work.

Working from the side can make stepladders unstable. Do not overreach

Don't stand on the top three steps

Stepladder is fully open

Locked open firm and level on the ground

Using a stepladder correctly

Trestles

This is a working platform used for work of a slightly longer duration.

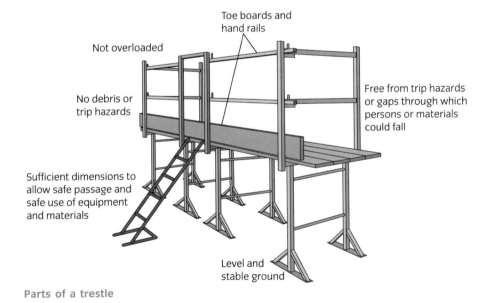

Not overloaded

Toe boards and hand rails

No debris or trip hazards

Free from trip hazards or gaps through which persons or materials could fall

Sufficient dimensions to allow safe passage and safe use of equipment and materials

Level and stable ground

Parts of a trestle

Tower scaffold

These are usually proprietary (manufactured) and are made from galvanised steel or lightweight aluminium alloy. They must be erected by someone competent in the erection and dismantling of mobile scaffolds.

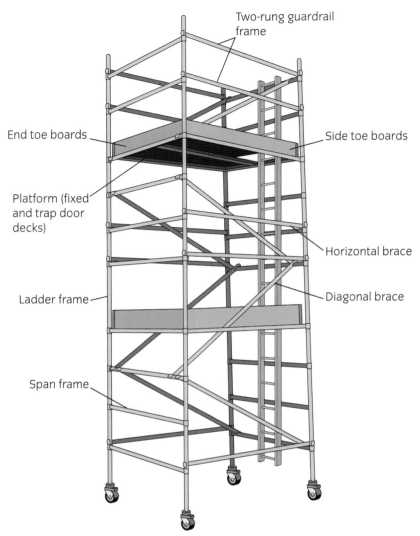

Two-rung guardrail frame

End toe boards

Side toe boards

Platform (fixed and trap door decks)

Horizontal brace

Ladder frame

Diagonal brace

Span frame

Parts of a tower scaffold

To use a tower scaffold safely:

- Always read and follow the manufacturer's instruction manual.
- Only use the equipment for what it is designed for.
- The wheels or feet of the tower must be in contact with a firm surface.
- Outriggers should be used to increase stability. The maximum height given in the manufacturer's instructions must not be exceeded.
- The platform must not be overloaded.
- The platform should be unloaded (and reduced in height if required) before it is moved.
- Never move a platform, even a small distance, if it is occupied.

INDUSTRY TIP

Remember, even a mobile access tower should have toe boards and guard rails fitted at all times when in use.

Tubular scaffold

This comes in two types:

- independent scaffold has two sets of standards or uprights
- putlog scaffold is built into the brickwork.

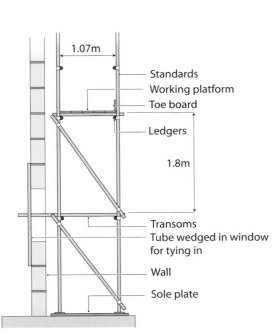

1.07m

Standards
Working platform
Toe board

Ledgers

1.8m

Transoms
Tube wedged in window for tying in

Wall

Sole plate

Independent tubular scaffold

Standards
Working platform
Toe board
Putlogs

At least 75mm

Ledgers
Putlogs
1.8m

Horizontal tie
Tube wedged in window for tying in

Wall

Sole plate

Putlog tubular scaffold

Tubular scaffold is erected by specialist scaffolding companies and often requires structural calculations. Only trained and competent scaffold erectors should alter scaffolding. Access to a scaffold is usually via a tied ladder with three rungs projecting above the step off at platform level.

OUR HOUSE

You have been asked to complete a job that requires gaining access to the roof level of a two-storey building. What equipment would you choose to get access to the work area? What things would you take into consideration when choosing the equipment? Take a look at 'Our House' as a guide for working on a two-storey building.

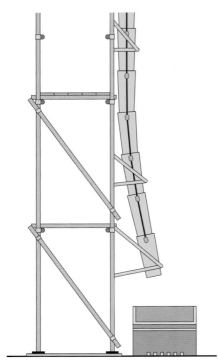

A debris chute for scaffolding

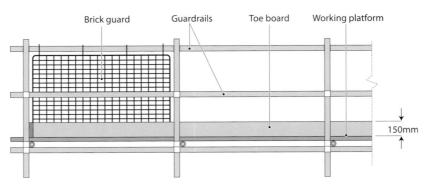

A safe working platform on a tubular scaffold

All scaffolding must:

- not have any gaps in the handrail or toe boards
- have a safe system for lifting any materials up to the working height
- have a safe system of debris removal.

Fall protection devices include:

- harnesses and lanyards
- safety netting
- air bags.

A harness and lanyard or safety netting will stop a person falling too far, leaving them suspended in the air. Air bags (commonly known as 'bouncy castles') are set up on the ground and inflated. If a person falls, they will have a soft landing. Air bags have fallen out of favour somewhat as some operatives use them as an easy way to get off the working platform – not the purpose they were intended for!

Using a scissor lift at height

LIFTING OPERATIONS AND LIFTING EQUIPMENT REGULATIONS (LOLER) 1998

The Lifting Operations and Lifting Equipment Regulations (LOLER) 1998 put responsibility upon employers to ensure that the lifting equipment provided for use at work is:

- strong and stable enough for the particular use and marked to indicate safe working loads
- positioned and installed to minimise any risks
- used safely, ie the work is planned, organised and performed by competent people
- subject to on-going thorough examination and, where appropriate, inspection by competent people.

THE CONTROL OF VIBRATION AT WORK REGULATIONS 2005

Vibration white finger or hand–arm vibration syndrome (HAVS) (see page 23) is caused by using vibrating tools such as hammer drills, vibrating pokers or hand-held breakers over a long period of time. The most efficient and effective way of controlling exposure to hand–arm vibration is to look for new or alternative work methods that remove or reduce exposure to vibration.

Follow these steps to reduce the effects of HAVS:

■ Always use the right tool for each job.

■ Check tools before using them to make sure they have been properly maintained and repaired to avoid increased vibration caused by faults or general wear.

■ Make sure cutting tools are kept sharp so that they remain efficient.

■ Reduce the amount of time you use a tool in one go, by doing other jobs in between.

■ Avoid gripping or forcing a tool or work piece more than you have to.

■ Encourage good blood circulation by:
  • keeping warm and dry (when necessary, wear gloves, a hat, waterproofs and use heating pads if available)
  • giving up or cutting down on smoking because smoking reduces blood flow
  • massaging and exercising your fingers during work breaks.

Damage from HAVS can include the inability to do fine work and cold can trigger painful finger blanching attacks (when the ends of your fingers go white).

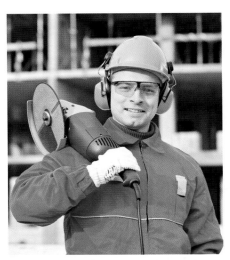

An operative taking a rest from using a power tool

Don't use power tools for longer than you need to

CONSTRUCTION SITE HAZARDS

DANGERS ON CONSTRUCTION SITES

Study the drawing of a building site. There is some demolition taking place, as well as construction. How many hazards can you find? Discuss your answers.

Dangers	Discussion points
Head protection	The operatives are not wearing safety helmets, which would prevent them from hitting their head or from falling objects.
Poor housekeeping	The site is very untidy. This can result in slips, trips and falls and can pollute the environment. An untidy site gives a poor company image. Offcuts and debris should be regularly removed and disposed of according to site policy and recycled if possible.
Fire	There is a fire near a building; this is hazardous. Fires can easily become uncontrollable and spread. There is a risk to the structure and, more importantly, a risk of operatives being burned. Fires can also pollute the environment.

Dangers	Discussion points
Trip hazards	Notice the tools and debris on the floor. The scaffold has been poorly constructed. There is a trip hazard where the scaffold boards overlap.
Chemical spills	There is a drum leaking onto the ground. This should be stored properly – upright and in a lockable metal shed or cupboard. The leak poses a risk of pollution and of chemical burns to operatives.
Falls from height	The scaffold has handrails missing. The trestle working platform has not been fitted with guard rails. None of the operatives is wearing a hard hat for protection either.
Noise	An operative is using noisy machinery with other people nearby. The operative should be wearing ear PPE, as should those working nearby. Better still, they should be working elsewhere if at all possible, isolating them-selves from the noise.
Electrical	Some of the wiring is 240V as there is no trans-former, it's in poor repair and it's also dragging through liquid. This not only increases the risk of electrocution but is also a trip hazard.
Asbestos or other hazardous substances	Some old buildings contain **asbestos** roofing which can become a hazard when being demolished or removed. Other potential hazards include lead paint or mould spores. If a potentially hazardous material is discovered a supervisor must be notified immediately and work must stop until the hazard is dealt with appropriately.

Asbestos

A naturally occurring mineral that was commonly used for a variety of purposes including: **insulation**, fire protection, roofing and guttering. It is extremely hazardous and can cause a serious lung disease known as asbestosis

Insulation

A material that reduces or prevents the transmission of heat

Cables can be a trip hazard on site

Boiler suit

Hand cleaner

PERSONAL HYGIENE

Working in the construction industry can be very physical, and it's likely to be quite dirty at times. Therefore you should take good care with your personal hygiene. This involves washing well after work. If contaminants are present, then wearing a protective suit, such as a boiler suit, that you can take off before you go home will prevent contaminants being taken home with you.

You should also wash your hands after going to the toilet and before eating. This makes it safer to eat and more pleasant for others around you. The following steps show a safe and hygienic way to wash your hands.

STEP 1 Apply soap to hands from the dispenser.

STEP 2 Rub the soap into a lather and cover your hands with it, including between your fingers.

STEP 3 Rinse hands under a running tap removing all of the soap from your hands.

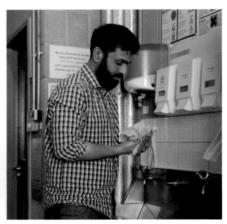

STEP 4 Dry your hands using disposable towels. Put the towels in the bin once your hands are dry.

WORKING WITH ELECTRICITY

Electricity is a very useful energy resource but it can be very dangerous. Electricity must be handled with care! Only trained, competent people can work with electrical equipment.

THE DANGERS OF USING ELECTRICAL EQUIPMENT

The main dangers of electricity are:

- shock and burns (a 230V shock can kill)

- electrical faults which could cause a fire

- an explosion where an electrical spark has ignited a flammable gas.

VOLTAGES

Generally speaking, the lower the voltage the safer it is. However, a low voltage is not necessarily suitable for some machines, so higher voltages can be found. On site, 110V (volts) is recommended and this is the voltage rating most commonly used in the building industry. This is converted from 230V by use of a transformer.

230V (commonly called 240V) domestic voltage is used on site as battery chargers usually require this voltage. Although 230V is often used in workshops, 110V is recommended.

410V (otherwise known as 3 phase) is used for large machinery, such as joinery shop equipment.

Voltages are nominal, ie they can vary slightly.

110V 1 phase – yellow

230V 1 phase – blue

410V 3 phase – red

BATTERY POWER

Battery power is much safer than mains power. Many power tools are now available in battery-powered versions. They are available in a wide variety of voltages from 3.6V for a small screwdriver all the way up to 36V for large masonry drills.

The images on the next page are all examples of battery-powered tools you may come across in your workplace or place of training.

Battery drill · Battery-powered planer · Battery-powered jigsaw

WIRING

The wires inside a cable are made from copper, which conducts electricity. The copper is surrounded by a plastic coating that is colour coded. The three wires in a cable are the live (brown), which works with the neutral (blue) to conduct electricity, making the appliance work. The earth (green and yellow stripes) prevents electrocution if the appliance is faulty or damaged.

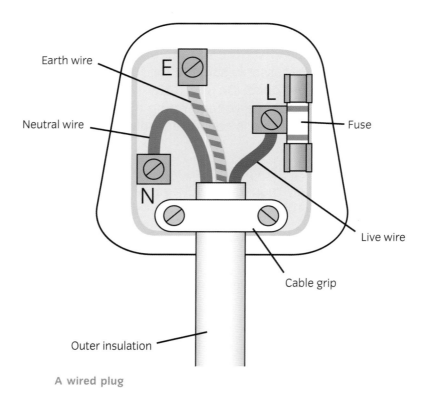

A wired plug

POWER TOOLS AND CHECKS

Power tools should always be checked before use. Always inform your supervisor if you find a fault. The tool will need to be repaired, and the tool needs to be kept out of use until then. The tool might be taken away, put in the site office and clearly labelled 'Do not use'.

Power tool checks include:

- *Look for the portable appliance testing (PAT) label*: PAT is a regular test carried out by a competent person (eg a qualified electrician) to ensure the tool is in a safe electrical condition. A sticker is placed on the tool after it has been tested. Tools that do not pass the PAT are taken out of use.

 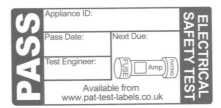

PAT testing labels

Cable protection

- *Cable*: Is it damaged? Is there a repair? Insulation tape may be hiding a damaged cable. Damaged cables must be replaced.

- *Casing*: Is the casing cracked? Plastic casings ensure the tool is double-insulated. This means the live parts inside are safely shielded from the user. A cracked casing will reduce the protection to the user and will require repair.

- *Guards and tooling*: Are guards in place? Is the tooling sharp?

- *Electricity supply leads*: Are they damaged? Are they creating a trip hazard? You need to place them in such a way that they do not make a trip hazard. Are they protected from damage? If they are lying on the floor with heavy traffic crossing them, they must be covered.

- *Use appropriate equipment for the size of the job*: For example, too many splitters can result in a web of cables.

- *Storage*: After use, power tools and equipment should be stored correctly. Tools must be returned to the boxes, including all the guards and parts. Cables need to be wound onto reels or neatly coiled as they can become tangled very easily.

Cable reel

INDUSTRY TIP

Remember, always fully unroll an extension lead before use because it could overheat and cause a fire.

FIRE

Fire needs three things to start; if just one of them is missing there will be no fire. If all are present then a fire is unavoidable:

1 *Oxygen*: A naturally occurring gas in the air that combines with flammable substances under certain circumstances.

2 *Heat*: A source of fire, such as a hot spark from a grinder or naked flame.

3 *Fuel*: Things that will burn such as acetone, timber, cardboard or paper.

The fire triangle

If you have heat, fuel and oxygen you will have a fire. Remove any of these and the fire will go out.

PREVENTING THE SPREAD OF FIRE

Being tidy will help prevent fires starting and spreading. For instance:

- Wood offcuts should not be left in big piles or standing up against a wall. Instead, useable offcuts should be stored in racks.

- Put waste into the allocated disposal bins or skips.

- Always replace the cap on unused fuel containers when you put them away. Otherwise they are a potential source of danger.

- Flammable liquids (not limited to fuel-flammable liquids) such as oil based paint, thinners and oil must be stored in a locked metal cupboard or shed.

FIRE

FIRE

Fire needs three things to start; if just one of them is missing there will be no fire. If all are present then a fire is unavoidable:

1 *Oxygen*: A naturally occurring gas in the air that combines with flammable substances under certain circumstances.

2 *Heat*: A source of fire, such as a hot spark from a grinder or naked flame.

3 *Fuel*: Things that will burn such as acetone, timber, cardboard or paper.

The fire triangle

If you have heat, fuel and oxygen you will have a fire. Remove any of these and the fire will go out.

PREVENTING THE SPREAD OF FIRE

Being tidy will help prevent fires starting and spreading. For instance:

- Wood offcuts should not be left in big piles or standing up against a wall. Instead, useable offcuts should be stored in racks.

- Put waste into the allocated disposal bins or skips.

- Always replace the cap on unused fuel containers when you put them away. Otherwise they are a potential source of danger.

- Flammable liquids (not limited to fuel-flammable liquids) such as oil based paint, thinners and oil must be stored in a locked metal cupboard or shed.

38

THE CITY & GUILDS TEXTBOOK

- Smoking around flammable substances should be avoided.

- Dust can be explosive, so when doing work that produces wood dust it is important to use some form of extraction and have good ventilation.

FIRE EXTINGUISHERS AND THEIR USES

You need to know where the fire extinguishers and blankets are located and which fire extinguishers can be used on different fires. The table below shows the different classes of fire and which extinguisher to use in each case.

Class of fire	Materials	Type of extinguisher
A	Wood, paper, hair, textiles	Water, foam, dry powder, wet chemical
B	Flammable liquids	Foam, dry powder, CO_2
C	Flammable gases	Dry powder, CO_2
D	Flammable metals	Specially formulated dry powder
E	Electrical fires	CO_2, dry powder
F	Cooking oils	Wet chemical, fire blanket

Fire blanket

INDUSTRY TIP

Remember, although all fire extinguishers are red, they each have a different coloured label to identify their contents.

CO_2 extinguisher

Dry powder extinguisher

Water extinguisher

Foam extinguisher

It is important to use the correct extinguisher for the type of fire as using the wrong one could make the danger much worse, eg using water on an electrical fire could lead to the user being electrocuted!

EMERGENCY PROCEDURES

In an emergency, people tend to panic. If an emergency were to occur, such as fire, discovering a bomb or some other security problem, would you know what to do? It is vital to be prepared in case of an emergency.

It is your responsibility to know the emergency procedures on your work site:

- If you discover a fire or other emergency you will need to raise the alarm:
  - You will need to tell a nominated person. Who is this?
  - If you are first on the scene you will have to ring the emergency services on 999.

- Be aware of the alarm signal. Is it a bell, a voice or a siren?

- Where is the assembly point? You will have to proceed to this point in an orderly way. Leave all your belongings behind; they may slow you or others down.

- At the assembly point, there will be someone who will ensure everyone is out safely and will do so by taking a count. Do you know who this person is? If during a fire you are not accounted for, a firefighter may risk their life to go into the building to look for you.

- How do you know it's safe to re-enter the building? You will be told by the appointed person. It's very important that you do not re-enter the building until you are told to do so.

Emergency procedure sign

ACTIVITY

What is the fire evacuation procedure at your workplace or place of training?

SIGNS AND SAFETY NOTICES

The law sets out the types of safety signs needed on a construction site. Some signs that warn us about danger and others tell us what to do to stay safe.

The following table describes five basic types of sign.

Type of sign	Description
Prohibition	These signs are red and white. They are round. They signify something that must *not* be done.
Mandatory	These signs are blue. They are round. They signify something that *must* be done.

Type of sign	Description
Caution 	These signs are yellow and black. They are triangular. These give warning of hazards.
Safe condition 	These signs are green. They are usually square or rectangular. They tell you the safe way to go, or what to do in an emergency.
Supplementary 	These white signs are square or rectangular and give additional important information. They usually accompany the signs above.

Case Study: Graham and Anton

An old barn had planning passed in order for it to be converted into a dwelling.

Keith, the contractor, was appointed and the small building company turned up first thing Monday morning.

Graham, the foreman, took a short ladder off the van to access the building's asbestos and slate roof to inspect its condition. The ladder just reached fascia level. As Graham stepped off onto the roof the ladder fell away, leaving him stranded. Luckily for him, Anton the apprentice, who was sitting in the van at the time noticed what had happened and rushed over to put the ladder back up.

While inspecting the whole roof Graham found that the asbestos roof covering was rather old and had become brittle over time, especially the clear plastic roof light sections. It was also clear upon close inspection that the ridge had holes in it and was leaking water. On the slated area of the roof it was noted that many slates were loose and some of them had fallen away leaving the battens and rafters exposed which was leading to severe decay of the timbers.

It was decided that the whole roof needed to be replaced.

- Was the survey carried out safely?

- What accidents could have happened during the survey?

- What could have been done to make the whole operation safer?

- What is the builder's general view of safety?

- How would you carry out the roof work in a safe fashion?

Work through the following questions to check your learning.

1   Which one of the following must be filled out prior to carrying out a site task?

   a   Invoice.

   b   Bill of quantities.

   c   Risk assessment.

   d   Schedule.

2   Which one of the following signs shows you something you **must** do?

   a   Green circle.

   b   Yellow triangle.

   c   White square.

   d   Blue circle.

3   Two parts of the fire triangle are heat and fuel. What is the third?

   a   Nitrogen.

   b   Oxygen.

   c   Carbon dioxide.

   d   Hydrogen sulphite.

4   Which of the following types of fire extinguisher would **best** put out an electrical fire?

   a CO_2.

   b   Powder.

   c   Water.

   d   Foam.

5   Which piece of health and safety legislation is designed to protect an operative from ill health and injury when using solvents and adhesives?

   a   Manual Handling Operations Regulations 1992.

   b   Control of Substances Hazardous to Health (COSHH) Regulations 2002.

   c   Health and Safety (First Aid) Regulations 1981.

   d   Lifting Operations and Lifting Equipment Regulations (LOLER) 1998.

6   What is the correct angle at which to lean a ladder against a wall?

   a   70°.

   b   80°.

   c   75°.

   d   85°.

7   Which are the **most** important pieces of PPE to use when using a disc cutter?

   a   Overalls, gloves and boots.

   b   Boots, head protection and overalls.

   c   Glasses, hearing protection and dust mask.

   d   Gloves, head protection and boots.

8   Which one of the following is **not** a lifting aid?

   a   Wheelbarrow.

   b   Kerb lifter.

   c   Gin lift.

   d   Respirator.

9   Which one of the following is a 3 phase voltage?

   a   410V.

   b   230V.

   c   240V.

   d   110V.

10 Above what noise level must you wear ear protection?

   a   75dB(a).

   b   80dB(a).

   c   85dB(a).

   d   90dB(a).

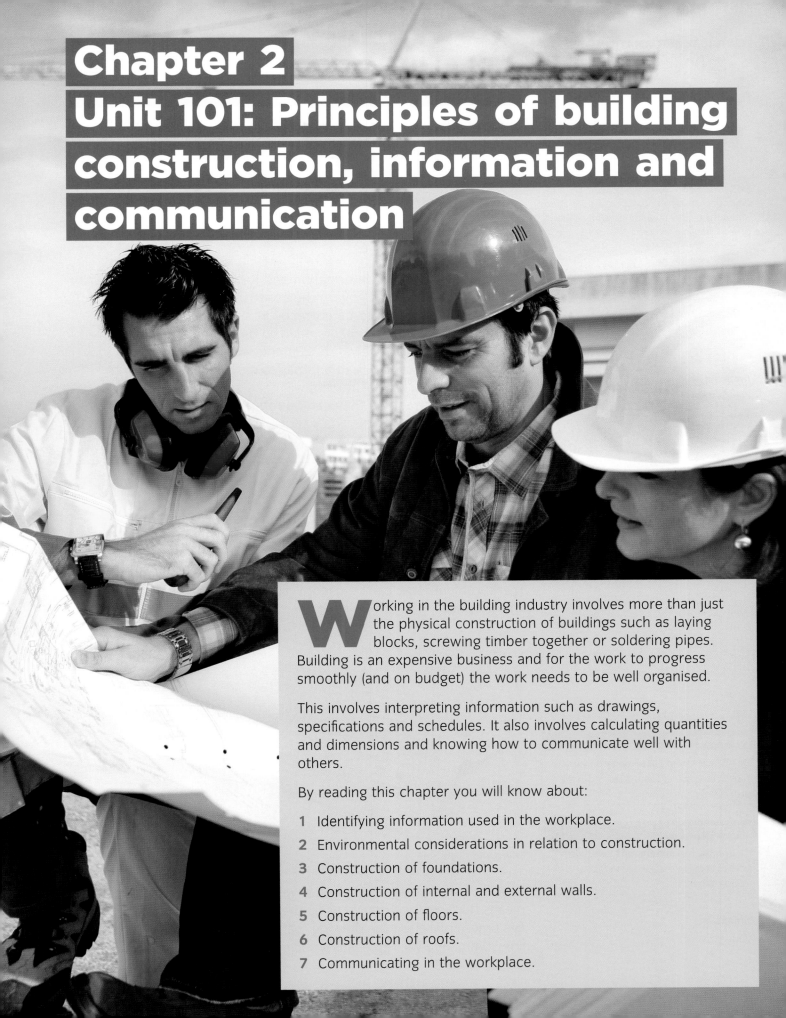

Chapter 2
Unit 101: Principles of building construction, information and communication

Working in the building industry involves more than just the physical construction of buildings such as laying blocks, screwing timber together or soldering pipes. Building is an expensive business and for the work to progress smoothly (and on budget) the work needs to be well organised.

This involves interpreting information such as drawings, specifications and schedules. It also involves calculating quantities and dimensions and knowing how to communicate well with others.

By reading this chapter you will know about:

1 Identifying information used in the workplace.
2 Environmental considerations in relation to construction.
3 Construction of foundations.
4 Construction of internal and external walls.
5 Construction of floors.
6 Construction of roofs.
7 Communicating in the workplace.

TECHNICAL INFORMATION

This section will discuss the three main sources of technical information that are used when constructing buildings:

- working drawings and **specifications**
- schedules
- **bill of quantities**.

These are all essential information and form the contract documents (those that govern the construction of a building). All documentation needs to be correctly interpreted and correctly used. The contract documents need to be looked after and stored (filed) correctly and safely. If documents are left lying around they will become difficult to read and pages may be lost, leading to errors. The contract documents will need to be **archived** at the end of the contract, so they can be referred back to in case of any query or dispute over the work carried out or the materials used.

DRAWING SCALES

It is impossible to fit a full-sized drawing of a building onto a sheet of paper, so it is necessary to **scale** (shrink) the size of the building to enable it to fit. The building has to be shrunk in proportion; this makes it possible to convert measurements on the drawing into real measurements that can be used. Scale rules are made specifically for this purpose.

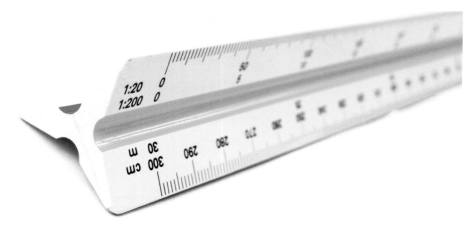

Triangular scale rule

How do scale rules work? Let's say we are using a scale of 1:5. That means that what we draw – using the sizes on the scale rule – will be five times smaller on the drawing than the object's actual size. So, a line 30mm long will represent an object 150mm long (30 × 5 = 150).

Specification

A contract document that gives information about the quality of materials and standards of workmanship required

Bill of quantities

A document containing quantities, descriptions and cost of works and resources

Archived

Kept in storage

Scale

The ratio of the size on a drawing to the size of the real thing that it represents

INDUSTRY TIP

Do not scale from photocopies because these can easily become distorted in the process of photocopying.

INDUSTRY TIP

If a drawing has **dimensions**, use these instead of using a scale rule to take a measurement.

Dimension

A measurement

The **British Standards Institute's** BS 1192 (Drawing office practice) gives a range of standard scales that are used for various drawing types and scale rules are manufactured to meet this purpose.

British Standards Institute

The British Standards Institute (BSI) is the UK authority that develops and publishes standards in the UK

SCALES IN COMMON USE

Scale	Use
1:1	Full size (used for rods)
1:2 1:5 1:10	Building details
1:20 1:50 1:100 1:200	Plans, elevations and sections
1:200 1:500 1:1250	Site plans
1:1250 1:2500	Location plans

The documents these scales are used for are described on pages 49–51.

ACTIVITY

Work out the following:

Scale size	Scale	Actual size
10mm	1:10	100mm
25mm	1:20	a)
b)	1:50	300mm
50mm	1:200	c)

Answers: a) 500mm, b) 6mm, c) 10m

DATUM POINTS

Heights of buildings and the relative heights of components within the building are calculated from a common **datum point**. Datum points are determined by transferring a known fixed height from a bench mark. There are two types of datum point:

- A permanent Ordnance bench mark (OBM) is a given height on an Ordnance Survey map. This fixed height is described as a value, eg so many metres above sea level (as calculated from the average sea height at Newlyn, Cornwall).

- A temporary bench mark (TBM) is set up on site.

Datum point

A fixed point or height from which reference levels can be taken. The datum point is used to transfer levels across a building site. It represents the finished floor level (FFL) on a dwelling

Ordnance and temporary bench marks

ACTIVITY

Find your local OBM or your site TBM.

BASIC DRAWING SYMBOLS (HATCHINGS)

Standard symbols, also known as hatching symbols, are used on drawings as a means of passing on information simply. If all the parts of a building were labelled in writing, the drawing would soon become very crowded. Additionally, it is important to use standard symbols so that everyone can read them and it means the same to everyone. The following images are just some of the standard symbols used.

Sink	Sinktop	Wash basin	Bath	Shower tray
WC	Window	Door	Radiator	Lamp
Switch	Socket	North symbol	Sawn timber (unwrot)	Concrete
Insulation	Brickwork	Blockwork	Stonework	Earth (subsoil)
Cement screed	Damp proof course/ membrane	Hardcore	Hinging position of windows	Stairs up and down
Timber – softwood. Machined all round (wrot)	Timber – hardwood. Machined all round (wrot)			

INFORMATION SOURCES

Type of drawing	Description
Location drawings	Usually prepared by an **architect** or **architectural technician**. Show the location of the building plot, position of the building and areas within the building. The term location drawings covers all of the drawings in this table.
Block plans 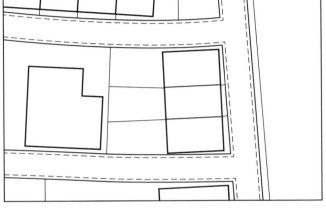	Show the proposed development in relation to its surrounding properties. The scales used are 1:1250 or 1:2500. Very little detail is available from this type of plan. The direction North is usually shown.
Site plans 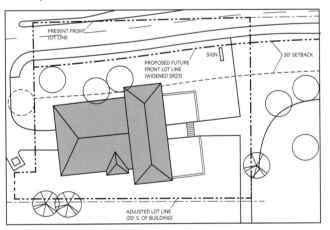	Show the plot in more detail, with drain runs, road layouts and the size and position of the existing building (and any extensions proposed) in relation to the property boundary. A scale of 1:500 or 1:200 is used. The Planning Portal sometimes refers to site plans as block plans, but the two types of plan have been distinguished in this book.

Architect

A trained professional who designs a structure and represents the client who wants the structure built. They are responsible for the production of the working drawings. They supervise the construction of buildings or other large structures

Architectural technician

A draftsperson who works in an architectural practice

Type of drawing	Description
Floor plans 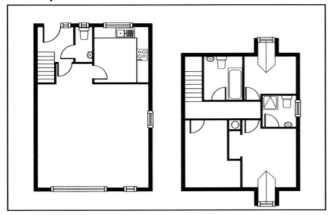	Show the positioning of walls, size of rooms along with the positioning of elements within the building such as units.
Elevations 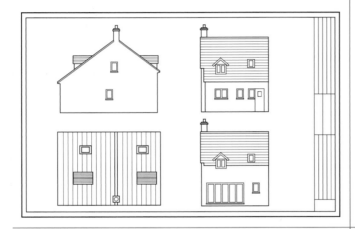	Show a building from a particular side and show the positioning of features such as doors and windows.
Sections 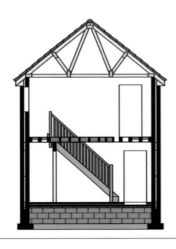	Show in greater detail what the section of a component looks like and how it might fit in relation to another component. A typical example would be a cross-section of a window showing the size of the features and how they fit together. Using these drawings it is possible to determine the positions of rooms, windows, doors, kitchen units and so on. Elevations are shown. These drawings are more detailed, and are often scaled to provide construction measurements. Some of the scales used are 1:200, 1:100, 1:50, 1:10, 1:5 and 1:1. A scale of 1:1 is full size.

Type of drawing	Description
Construction drawings (Detail drawings) 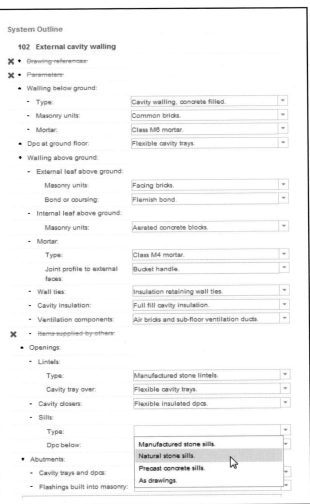	Show details of construction, normally as a cross-section.

SPECIFICATIONS

A specification accompanies the working drawings. It gives further information that cannot be shown on the drawings, because the drawings need to be clear and not covered in notes. A specification would include information such as:

- the colour of paint required

- a specific timber species

- the brick type required

- the plaster finish required.

It is prepared by construction professionals such as architects and building services engineers. They can be produced from previous project specifications, in-house documents or master specifications such as the National Building Specification (NBS). The NBS is owned by the Royal Institute of British Architects (RIBA).

Example of a specification

COMPONENT RANGE DRAWINGS

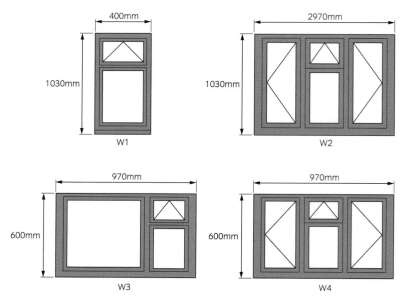

Component range drawing of windows

A component range drawing shows the range of components available from a manufacturer. It includes:

- sizes available

- coding for ordering purposes

- availability (whether it can be bought off-the-shelf or if pre-ordering is required).

Availability is particularly important when planning delivery dates. Schedules reference this type of drawing.

SCHEDULES

A schedule is used to record repeated design information that applies to a range of components or fittings, such as:

- windows

- doors

- kitchen units

- joinery fittings.

A schedule is mainly used on bigger sites where there are multiples of several designs of houses, with each type having different components and fittings. It avoids the wrong component or fitting being put in the wrong house.

A schedule is usually used in conjunction with a component range drawing and a floor plan.

In a typical plan, the doors and windows are labelled D1, D2, W1, W2 etc. These components would be included in the schedule, which would provide additional information on them. For example see the following schedule.

Master Internal Door Schedule							
Ref:	Door size	S.O. width	S.O. height	Lintel type	FD30	Self closing	Floor level
D1	838×1981	900	2040	BOX	Yes	Yes	GROUND FLOOR
D2	838×1981	900	2040	BOX	Yes	Yes	GROUND FLOOR
D3	762×1981	824	2040	BOX	No	No	GROUND FLOOR
D4	838×1981	900	2040	N/A	Yes	No	GROUND FLOOR
D5	838×1981	900	2040	BOX	Yes	Yes	GROUND FLOOR
D6	762×1981	824	2040	BOX	Yes	Yes	FIRST FLOOR
D7	762×1981	824	2040	BOX	Yes	Yes	FIRST FLOOR
D8	762×1981	824	2040	N/A	Yes	No	FIRST FLOOR
D9	762×1981	824	2040	BOX	Yes	Yes	FIRST FLOOR
D10	762×1981	824	2040	N/A	No	No	FIRST FLOOR
D11	686×1981	748	2040	N/A	Yes	No	SECOND FLOOR
D12	762×1981	824	2040	BOX	Yes	Yes	SECOND FLOOR
D13	762×1981	824	2040	100 HD BOX	Yes	Yes	SECOND FLOOR
D14	686×1981	748	2040	N/A	No	No	SECOND FLOOR

Example of a schedule

BILL OF QUANTITIES

A bill of quantities is produced by the quantity surveyor and describes everything that is required for the job based on the drawings, specification and schedules. A bill of quantities contains the following information:

- *Preliminaries*: General information including the client and architect, details of the work and descriptions of the site.

- *Preambles*: Like the specification, this outlines the quality and description of materials and workmanship, etc.

- *Measured quantities*: A description of how each task and material is to be measured, with measurements in metres (linear and square), hours, litres, kilogrammes and the number of components required.

The completed document is sent out to contractors who will then price the work and enter the costs into the blank spaces. The bill of quantities ensures that all the contractors are pricing for the job using the same information.

BILL OF QUANTITIES

(Assuming Civil Engineering Standard Method of Measurement (CESSM3) is used.)

Number	Item description	Unit	Quantity	Rate	Amount £	p
	CLASS A: GENERAL ITEMS					
	Specified Requirements					
	Testing of Materials					
A250	Testing of recycled and secondary aggregates	sum				
	Information to be provided by the Contractor					
A290	Production of Materials Management Plan	sum				
	Method Related Charges					
	Recycling Plant / Equipment					
A339.01	Mobilise; Fixed	sum				
A339.02	Operate; Time-Related	sum				
A339.03	De-mobilise; Fixed	sum				
	CLASS D: DEMOLITION AND SITE CLEARANCE					
	Other Structures					
D522.01	Other structures; Concrete;	sum				
D522.02	Grading / processing of demolition material to produce recycled and secondary aggregates	m³	70			
D522.03	Disposal of demolition material offsite	m³	30			
	CLASS E: EARTHWORKS					
	Excavation Ancillaries					

Bill of quantities

WORK SCHEDULES

It is very important indeed that the progress of work is planned out. A work schedule or programme of work is an easy way of showing what work is to be carried out and when. This is usually shown in the form of a bar chart called a Gantt chart. The chart lists the tasks that need to be done on the left-hand side and shows a timeline across the top. The site manager or trade supervisors can quickly tell from looking at this chart:

- if work is keeping to schedule

- what materials, equipment and labour are required

- when they are required.

Materials very often have a **lead-in time** and so cannot be delivered immediately. These need to be ordered and delivered at the correct time. Labour planning is also required as the trades may be working elsewhere when needed.

INDUSTRY TIP

Use of a planning document such as a Gantt chart will reduce waste and ensure effective use of labour.

Lead-in time

The time taken between ordering an item and it being delivered

Task	Time (days)						
	1	**2**	**3**	**4**	**5**	**6**	**7**
Prepare the ground	▒	▒					
Spread foundations			▒	▒			
Lay cables for services				▒	▒		
Build walls up to DPC						▒	▒
Proposed time in green							

Gantt chart

CALCULATING QUANTITIES FOR MATERIALS

Calculations are required throughout the building process. It is important that these calculations are accurate, as mistakes can be very expensive. A company can lose a lot of money if it underestimates:

- the amount of materials required

- how much they cost

- how long it will take to complete a job.

It could also lead to the company gaining a bad reputation for not being able to complete a job on time and in budget.

Materials are usually better priced if bought in bulk, whereas a buy-as-you go approach can cost more.

Consider these points when buying materials:

- Is there sufficient storage room for delivered materials?

- Is there a risk of the materials being damaged if there is nowhere suitable to store them or if they are delivered too early?

- Will it be a problem to obtain the same style, colour or quality of product if they are not all ordered at the same time?

- Will over-ordering cause lots of wastage?

These and many other considerations will help determine when and in what quantity materials are ordered.

Some wastage is unavoidable. Allowances must be made for wastage, eg cut bricks that cannot be re-used, short ends of timber, partly full paint cans. Up to 5% waste is allowed for bricks and blocks and 10% for timber and paint.

It may be that all the materials are ordered by the office or supervisory staff, but you still need to know how to recognise and calculate material requirements. Deliveries have to be checked before the delivery note is signed and the driver leaves. Any discrepancies in the type or quantity of materials, or any materials that have arrived damaged, must be recorded on the delivery note and reported to the supervisor. Any discrepancies will need to be followed up and new delivery times arranged.

You must be able to identify basic materials and carry out basic calculations. You will often have to collect sufficient materials to carry out a particular operation. Being able to measure accurately will mean you can make the most economic use of materials and therefore reduce waste.

Deliveries must be checked before signing the delivery note

UNITS OF MEASUREMENT

The construction industry uses metric units as standard; however, you may come across some older measures called imperial units.

Units for measuring	Metric units	Imperial units
Length	millimetre (mm) metre (m) kilometre (km)	inch (in) or " eg 6" (6 inches) foot (ft) or ' eg 8' (8 foot)
Liquid	millilitre (ml) litre (l)	pint (pt)
Weight	gramme (g) kilogramme (kg) tonne (t)	pound (lb)

ACTIVITY

Look online to find out:
- What other imperial units are still commonly used?
- How many millimetres are there in an inch?
- How many litres are there in a gallon?

Units for measuring	Quantities	Example
Length	There are 1,000mm in 1m There are 1,000m in 1km	1mm × 1,000 = 1m 1m × 1,000 = 1km 6,250mm can be shown as 6.250m 6,250m can be shown as 6.250km
Liquid	There are 1,000ml in 1l	1ml × 1,000 = 1l
Weight	There are 1,000g in 1kg There are 1,000kg in 1t	1g × 1,000 = 1kg 1kg × 1,000 = 1t

CALCULATIONS

Four basic mathematical operations are used in construction calculations.

ADDITION

The addition of two or more numbers is shown with a plus sign (**+**).

Example

A stack of bricks is 3 bricks long and 2 bricks high. It contains 6 bricks.

$$3 + 3 = \mathbf{6}$$

More examples:

$$5 + 2 = \mathbf{7}$$

$$19 + 12 = \mathbf{31}$$

$$234 + 105 = \mathbf{339}$$

Pallet of bricks

SUBTRACTION

The reduction of one number by another number is shown with a minus sign (**−**).

Example

A pallet containing 100 bricks is delivered on site, but you only need 88 bricks. How many are left over?

$$100 - 88 = \mathbf{12}$$

More examples:

$$5 - 2 = \mathbf{3}$$

$$19 - 12 = \mathbf{7}$$

$$234 - 105 = \mathbf{129}$$

MULTIPLICATION

The scaling of one number by another number is shown with a multiplication sign (×).

Example

A stack of bricks is 3 bricks long and 2 bricks high. It contains 6 bricks.

$$3 \times 2 = \mathbf{6}$$

More examples:

$$19 \times 12 = \mathbf{228}$$

$$234 \times 10 = \mathbf{2,340}$$

$$234 \times 105 = \mathbf{24,570}$$

In the two last examples, the comma (,) is used to show we are in the thousands. In words we would say, twenty four thousand, five hundred and seventy.

DIVISION

Sharing one number by another number in equal parts (how many times it goes into the number) is shown with a division sign (÷).

Example

$$5 \div 2 = \mathbf{2.5}$$

$$36 \div 12 = \mathbf{3}$$

$$600 \div 4 = \mathbf{150}$$

LINEAR LENGTH

Linear means how long a number of items would measure from end to end if laid in a straight line. Examples of things that are calculated in linear measurements are:

- skirting board

- lengths of timber

- rope

- building line

- wallpaper.

We use this form of measurement when working out how much of one of the materials listed above we need, eg to find out how much

Skirting boards are calculated using linear measurements

A joiner measuring a room

Perimeter

The distance around an object or room

skirting board is required for a room. First, we need to measure the **perimeter** (sides) of a room. To find the linear length we add the length of all four sides together. This can be done in two ways: adding or multiplying.

Example 1

A site carpenter has been asked how many metres of skirting are required for the rooms below.

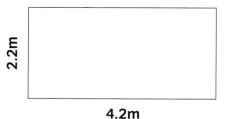

They can add all the sides together:

2.2 + 4.2 + 2.2 + 4.2 = 12.8m

Or, they can multiply each side by 2, and add them together:

(2.2 × 2) + (4.2 × 2) = 12.8m

Either way, **12.8m** is the correct answer.

Example 2

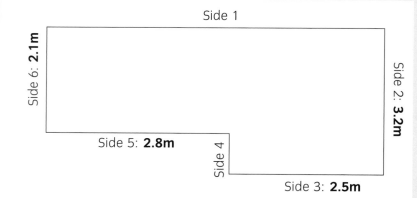

To work out the perimeter of this room we need to add all the sides together. In this example each side has been given a reference number, so all we need to do is add all the sides together, like this:

side 1 (side 3 + side 5) + side 2 + side 3 + side 4 (side 2 − side 6) + side 5 + side 6

Now, let's show the working out: (2.8 + 2.5) + 3.2 + 2.5 + (3.2 − 2.1) + 2.8 + 2.1 = 17m

The amount of skirting board required is **17m**.

Now let's put some door openings in. This symbol represents an opening.

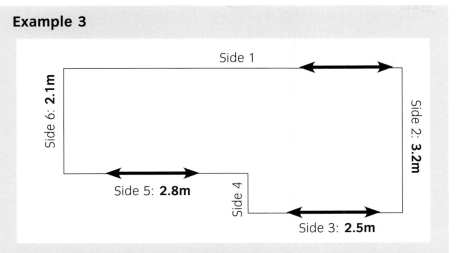

Example 3

On side 1 there is an opening 0.9m wide, on side 3 there is an opening 1.5m wide and on side 5 there is an opening 2.1m wide.

We know from Example 2 that the perimeter of the room is 17m. We now need to remove the openings. Skirting board will not be needed for the openings.

Step 1

Add together the lengths of the three combined openings:

0.9 + 1.5 + 2.1 = 4.5m

Step 2

Deduct this from 17m:

17 − 4.5 = 12.5m

The linear length of skirting board required is 12.5m.

Step 3

However, this calculation does not take into account any waste. We would normally add 10% extra to allow for waste:

12.5 + 10% = 12.5 + 1.25 = 13.75m

The total amount of skirting board required is **13.75m**.

PERCENTAGES

An easy way to find a percentage (%) of a number is to divide the number by 100 and then multiply it by the percentage you require.

Example

Increase 19m by 12%

$19 \div 100 = 0.19$

$0.19 \times 12 = 2.28$

$19 + 2.28 = 21.28$m

Total required **21.28m**.

ACTIVITY

1 Increase 49m by 10%
2 Increase 27m by 20%
3 Increase 34m by 17.5%
4 Decrease 22m by 5%

Answers: 1) 53.9m, 2) 32.4m, 3) 39.95m, 4) 20.9m

AREA

To find out how much material is required to cover a surface such as a **floor** or wall you need to calculate its area. Area is the measurements of a two-dimensional surface, eg the surface of floors, walls, glass or a roof.

Floors

The structured layers of a building, eg ground floor, first floor, second floor

To find the area of a surface you need to multiply its length by its width (L × W) or one side by the other. This will give you an answer which is expressed in square units (^{2}). For example, mm², m² or km².

Example 1

A bricklayer has been asked to work out the area of the floors below.

Side 1: **2.2m**

Side 2: **4.4m**

side 1 × side 2 = floor area

$2.2 \times 4.4 = 9.68$m²

The total floor area is **9.68m²**.

Irregularly shaped areas can be calculated by breaking up the area into sections that can be worked out easily, and then adding them together.

Example 2

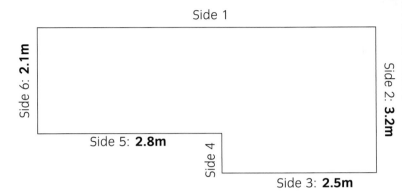

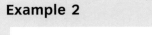

Irregularly shaped rooms can be split into sections to calculate the area

Step 1

Divide the area into two parts, and then calculate the area of each part. The easiest way to do this is to divide it into two smaller sections:

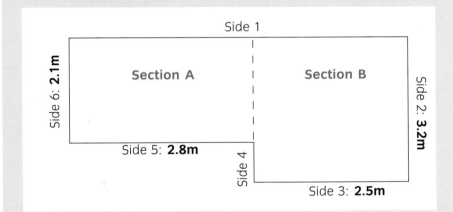

Step 2

Work out the areas of section A and section B:

section A: 2.1 × 2.8 = 5.88m²

section B: 2.5 × 3.2 = 8m²

Step 3

Add the areas of section A and section B together:

section A + section B = total floor area

5.88 + 8 = 13.88m²

The total floor area is **13.88m²**.

A tiler tiling a floor

ACTIVITY

Find the area of the following measurements:

1. 2.1m × 2.4m
2. 0.9m × 2.7m
3. 250mm × 3.4m

Answers: 1) 5.04m², 2) 2.43m², 3) 0.85m²

Now let's say the floor requires tiling. The tiler needs to calculate the number of floor tiles required.

Example 3

The size of each floor tile is 305mm × 305mm. We can also show this as 0.305m × 0.305m.

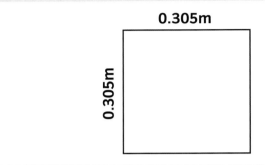

How many floor tiles are required for the floor area in Example 2? The total floor area is 13.88m².

Step 1

Calculate the area of one tile. As the floor area is given in m², we need to calculate the size of the tile in the same unit, ie m².

0.305 × 0.305 = 0.093m²

Step 2

Now you need to divide the total floor area by the area of one tile to find out the total number tiles required.

total floor area ÷ area of one tile = total number of tiles

13.88 ÷ 0.093 = 149.247 tiles

This number is rounded up to the next full tile, so a total of 150 floor tiles are required.

Step 3

However, this total does not allow for any waste.

Add 5% to allow for waste:

150 + 5% = 158 tiles (to the next full tile)

Let's look at the working out:

150 ÷ 100 = 1.5 tiles (this is 1%)

1.5 × 5 = 7.5 tiles (this is 5%)

5% of 150 tiles, rounded up to the next full tile, is 8 tiles.

Therefore **158 tiles** are required.

AREA OF A TRIANGLE

Sometimes you will be required to work out an area that includes a triangle.

Example 1

A painter has been asked to work out how much paint will be needed to paint the front of this house.

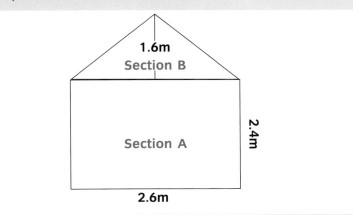

A decorator measuring a room

Step 1

Divide the area up into a rectangular section (section A) and a triangular section (section B).

Step 2

Find the area of section A:

$2.4 \times 2.6 = 6.24m^2$

The area of section A is 6.24m².

Step 3

Find the area of section B

The area of a triangle can be found by multiplying the base by the height, then dividing by 2.

(base × height) ÷ 2 = area

$2.6 \times 1.6 = 4.16$

$4.16 \div 2 = 2.08m^2$

The area of section B is 2.08m².

Step 4

area of section A + area of section B = total wall area

$6.24 + 2.08 = 8.32m^2$

The total wall area is **8.32m²**.

ACTIVITY

Look at the diagram. Work out the area of the wall in order to arrange the delivery of sufficient paint.

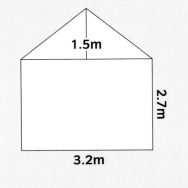

Answer: 11.04m²

Now let's look at the simple triangle below. It has three sides, A, B and C. Pythagorean theorem tells us that in a right-angled triangle the **hypotenuse** is equal to the sum of the square of the lengths of the two other sides, in other words $a^2 + b^2 = c^2$. In this example the hypotenuse is side C.

Using the Pythagorean theorem we can work out the length of any side.

Hypotenuse

The longest side of a right-angled triangle. It is always opposite the right angle

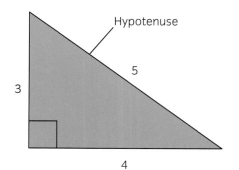

The hypotenuse

Example 1

If side A is 3m long and side B is 4m long, what is the length of side C?

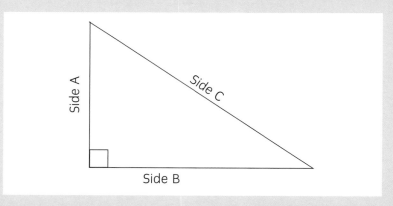

$3 \times 3 = 9$

$4 \times 4 = 16$

$9 + 16 = 25$

$\sqrt{25} = 5$

($\sqrt{}$ means square root. A square root of a number is the number that is multiplied by itself to make that number, in this case $5 \times 5 = 25$)

Side C is **5m** long.

INDUSTRY TIP

If a triangle has a small square in the corner, this shows you the corner is a right angle.

Example 2

A joiner has been asked to work out the length of a roof (side C).

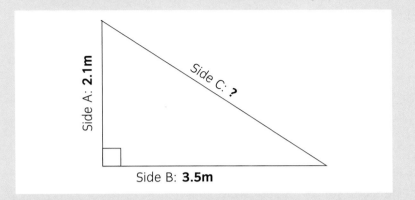

2.1 × 2.1 (side A) = 4.41

3.5 × 3.5 (side B) = 12.25

4.41 + 12.25 = 16.66

$\sqrt{16.66}$ = 4.08m

The length of side C is **4.08m**.

Example 3

A bricklayer needs to find the rise of a roof (side A).

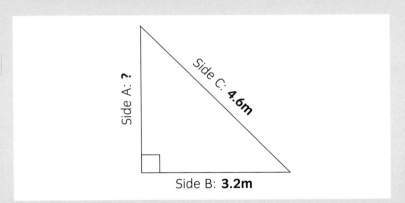

3.2 × 3.2 (side B) = 10.24

4.6 × 4.6 (side C) = 21.16

21.16 − 10.24 = 10.92

$\sqrt{10.92}$ = 3.30m

The length of side A is **3.3m**.

ACTIVITY

Use Pythagorean theorem to answer following questions:

1 What is the length of side B?

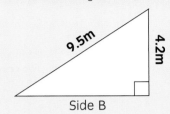

2 What is the length of side C?

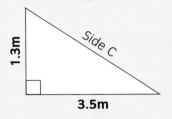

Answers: 1) 8.5m, 2) 3.73m

PERIMETERS AND AREAS OF CIRCLES

Circumference

The distance around the edge of a circle

Diameter

The length of a straight line going through the centre of a circle connecting two points on its circumference

Sometimes you are required to find the perimeter or **circumference** of a circle.

circumference of a circle = π × **diameter**

$$C = \pi d$$

π (or 'pi') is the number of times that the diameter of a circle will divide into the circumference.

π = 3.142

This is equal to the number of diameters in one revolution of a circle. It is the same for any sized circle.

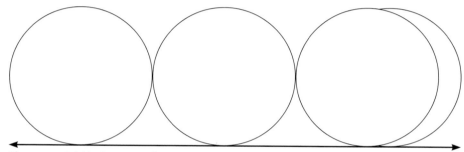

There are 3.142 diameters in one complete revolution

Example 1

A joiner is making a circular window that has a diameter of 600mm. Its circumference is:

0.600 × 3.142 = **1.885m**

The diameter of a circle from a given circumference is:

diameter = circumference ÷ π

Example 2

A window has a circumference of 2.250m. Its diameter is:

2.250 ÷ 3.142 = **0.716m** (or 716mm)

Radius

The length of a line from the centre to a point on the circumference of a circle. It is exactly half the length of the diameter

The area of a circle is found by:

area of a circle = π × **radius**² (radius is equal to half the diameter)

Example 3

A painter needs to paint a circle that is 1.2m in diameter and is required to find the area of the circle to enable them to order the correct quantity of paint.

1.2 ÷ 2 = **0.6m** (the radius)

3.142 × 0.6m² = **1.13m²**

VOLUME

The volume of an object is the total space it takes up, eg a tin of paint, a foundation for a wall or the capacity of a concrete mixer, and is shown as m³ (cubic metres). To find the volume of an object you must multiply length by width by height.

$$\text{volume} = \text{length} \times \text{width} \times \text{height}$$

Example 1

Each side of this cube is 1m. The total space it takes up is 1m³.

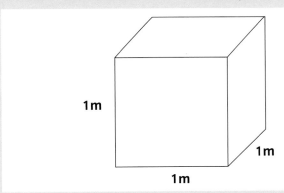

1m × 1m × 1m = **1m³**

Example 2

A bricklayer has been asked to work out how many m³ of **concrete** is required for a strip foundation. The size of the foundation is 3.2m long, 0.600m wide and 0.900m deep.

length × width × height = volume

3.2 × 0.600 × 0.900 = 1.728m³

The volume of concrete needed for the strip foundation is **1.728m³**.

A bricklayer taking levels

Concrete

Composed of cement, sand and stone, of varying size and in varying proportions

To work out the volume of a cylinder:

$$\text{volume} = \pi r^2 h \ (\pi \times r^2 \times h)$$

ACTIVITY

A bricklayer has been given two tasks:

1 Measure the volume of a strip foundation measuring 4.250m long, 1.1m wide and 1m deep.
2 Find the volume of four pile foundations (see page 80) each measuring 2.5m deep, with a diameter of 0.9m.

Work out the answers to the tasks.

Answers: 1) 4.675m³, 2) 6.36m²

Example 3

A joiner has a tin of presevative and needs to know its volume. The tin has a diameter of 250mm and a height of 700mm.

$\pi r^2 h \ (\pi \times r^2 \times h) = \text{volume}$

The radius (r) is half the diameter:

$250 \div 2 = 125mm$

$3.142 \times 0.125^2 \times 0.700 = 0.034m^3$

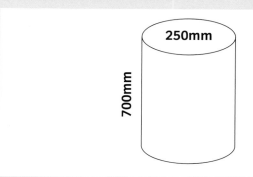

The volume of the tin of paint is **0.034m³**.

COMMUNICATION

Good communication is vital to the smooth running of any building project.

Communication involves sharing thoughts, information and ideas between people. For communication to be effective, information must be:

- given in a clear way
- received without misunderstanding.

It has been said that to be a good communicator it is just as important to be a good listener as it is to be a good speaker! Good communication leads to a safer and more efficient workplace, not to mention helping to maintain a pleasant working environment.

Most sites will have policies and procedures in place that govern the chain of command and communication between supervisory staff and workers.

INDUSTRY TIP

Before communicating something it is good to gather your thoughts. Have relevant information to hand, eg a drawing, and take notes if required.

ACTIVITY

A customer has asked for the best steps to take before painting the skirting board in their new home. You have been asked to reply to the customer and give advice on the best way for them to do this.

Decide on the best form of communication and list all the information you should give along with the stages they should follow.

WRITTEN COMMUNICATION

There are many methods of communication within the building industry. In this chapter we have discussed drawings, schedules and specifications etc. The architect uses these methods to communicate details about the building to the team who will **tender** for and erect the building.

Communication is usually electronic via email (with or without attachments) or through intranet sites. Drawings are very commonly distributed in electronic formats which are printed on to paper when required. Messages are often given via text.

Sometimes communication will be via a memorandum (memo), a written form of communication with a message.

Site rules, risk assessments and method statements (see Chapter 1) communicate safety information.

Tender

The process of supplying the client with a fixed quotation for the work

INDUSTRY TIP

Messages that are passed on by word of mouth are open to interpretation, so written messages often can be more clear.

SITE PAPERWORK

Communication on site is aided by the use of paperwork and without it no building site could operate. It is an important method of communication between operatives and supervisory staff, builders, architects and clients.

Type of paperwork	Description
Timesheet **Timesheet** Employer: CPF Building Co. Employee Name: Louise Miranda Week starting: 17/6/13 Date: 21/6/13 	Used to record the hours completed each day, and is usually the basis on which pay is calculated. Timesheets also help to work out how much the job has cost in working hours, and can give information for future estimating work when working up a tender.

Timesheet table:

Day	Job/Job Number	Start Time	Finish Time	Total Hours	Overtime
Monday	Penburthy, Falmouth 0897	9am	6pm	8	
Tuesday	Penburthy, Falmouth 0897	9am	6pm	8	
Wednesday	Penburthy, Falmouth 0897	8.30am	5.30pm	8	
Thursday	Trelawney, Truro 0901	11am	8pm	8	2
Friday	Trelawney, Truro 0901	11am	7pm	7	1
Saturday	Trelawney, Truro 0901	9am	1pm	4	
Totals				43	3

Employee's signature:_____

Supervisor's signature: _____

Type of paperwork	Description
Job sheet 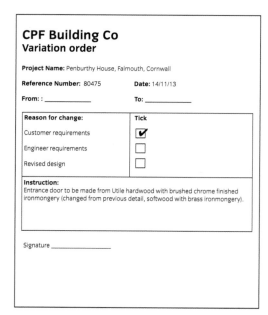	Gives details of a job to be carried out, sometimes with material requirements and hours given to complete the task.
Variation order **Confirmation notice** **Architect's instruction**	Sometimes alterations are made to the contract which changes the work to be completed, eg a client may wish to move a door position or request a different brick finish. This usually involves a variation to the cost. This work should not be carried out until a variation order and a confirmation notice have been issued. Architect's instructions are instructions given by an architect, first verbally and then in writing to a site agent as work progresses and questions inevitably arise over details and specifications.

Type of paperwork	Description
Requisition order **CPF Building Co** **Requisition order** Supplier Information: Construction Supplies Ltd Date: 9/12/13 Contract Address/Delivery Address: Penburthy House, Falmouth, Cornwall Tel number: 0207294333 Order Number: 26213263CPF <table><tr><th>Item number</th><th>Description</th><th>Quantity</th><th>Unit/Unit Price</th><th>Total</th></tr><tr><td>X22433</td><td>75mm 4mm gauge countersunk brass screws slotted</td><td>100</td><td>30p</td><td>£30</td></tr><tr><td>YK7334</td><td>Brass cups to suit</td><td>100</td><td>£5</td><td>£500</td></tr><tr><td>V23879</td><td>Sadikkens water based clear varnish</td><td>1 litre</td><td>£20.00</td><td>£20.00</td></tr><tr><td>Total:</td><td></td><td></td><td></td><td>£550.00</td></tr></table> Authorised by: Denzil Penburthy	Filled out to order materials from a supplier or central store. These usually have to be authorised by a supervisor before they can be used.
Delivery note **Construction Supplies Ltd** **Delivery note** Customer name and address: CPF Building Co Penburthy House Falmouth Cornwall Delivery Date: 16/12/13 Delivery time: 9am Order number: 26213263CPF <table><tr><th>Item number</th><th>Quantity</th><th>Description</th><th>Unit Price</th><th>Total</th></tr><tr><td>X22433</td><td>100</td><td>75mm 4mm gauge countersunk brass screws slotted</td><td>30p</td><td>£30</td></tr><tr><td>YK7334</td><td>100</td><td>Brass cups to suit</td><td>£5</td><td>£500</td></tr><tr><td>V23879</td><td>1 litre</td><td>Sadikkens water based clear varnish</td><td>£20</td><td>£20</td></tr></table> Subtotal £550.00 VAT 20% Total £660.00 Discrepancies: .... Customer Signature: .... Print name: .... Date:	Accompanies a delivery. Goods have to be checked for quantity and quality before the note is signed. Any discrepancies are recorded on the delivery note. Goods that are not suitable (because they are not as ordered or because they are of poor quality) can be refused and returned to the supplier.

Type of paperwork	Description
Delivery record **Davids & Co** **Monthly delivery record** Customer name and address: CPF Building Co Penburthy House Falmouth Cornwall Customer order date: 28th May 2013 <table><tr><th>Item number</th><th>Quantity</th><th>Description</th><th>Unit Price</th><th>Date Delivered</th></tr><tr><td>BS3647</td><td>2</td><td>1 ton bag of building sand</td><td>£60</td><td>3/6/13</td></tr><tr><td>CM4324</td><td>12</td><td>25kg bags of cement</td><td>£224</td><td>17/6/13</td></tr></table> Customer Signature: .... Print name: .... Date:	Every month a supplier will issue a delivery record that lists all the materials or hire used for that month.
Invoices **Davids & Co** **Invoice** Invoice number: 75856 PO number: 4700095685 Date: 2nd January 2014 Company name and address: Davids & Co 228 West Retail ParK Ivybridge Plymouth Customer name and address: CPF Building Co Penburthy House Falmouth Cornwall VAT registration number: 663694542 For: <table><tr><th>Item number</th><th>Quantity</th><th>Description</th><th>Unit Price</th></tr><tr><td>BS3647</td><td>2</td><td>1 ton bag of building sand</td><td>£30</td></tr><tr><td>CM4324</td><td>12</td><td>25kg bags of cement</td><td>£224</td></tr><tr><td colspan="3">Subtotal</td><td>£2748.00</td></tr><tr><td colspan="3">VAT</td><td>20%</td></tr><tr><td colspan="3">Total</td><td>£3297.60</td></tr></table> Please make cheques payable to Davids & Co Payment due in 30 days	Sent by a supplier. It lists the services or materials supplied along with the price the contractor is requested to pay. There will be a time limit within which to pay. Sometimes there will be a discount for quick payment or penalties for late payment.
Site diary 	This will be filled out daily. It records anything of note that happens on site such as deliveries, absences or occurrences, eg delay due to the weather.

VERBAL COMMUNICATION

Often, managers, supervisors, work colleagues and trades communicate verbally. This can be face to face or over a telephone. Although this is the most common form of communication, it is also the most unreliable.

Mistakes are often made while communicating verbally. The person giving the information might make an error. The person receiving the information might misunderstand something because the information is unclear or it is noisy in the background, or because they later forget the details of the conversation.

Confusion can be minimised by recording conversations or by using a form of written communication. If there is a record it can be used for future reference and help to clear up any misunderstandings.

ACTIVITY

Find a partner. Choose a particular health and safety issue – this may be something you have seen at your training centre or on site. Prepare some basic notes. Assume the roles of operative and supervisor and discuss the issue. Swap roles and discuss the problem again. Afterwards, write down the solutions on which you agreed.

What type of approach works best? Does preparation help? Why should you write down the results of your discussion?

TAKING A TELEPHONE MESSAGE

It is a good idea to take down details of telephone calls and many companies provide documentation for this purpose. When taking a message it is important to record the following details:

- *Content*: This is the most important part of the message – the actual information being relayed. Take and write down as many details as possible.

- *Date and time*: Messages are often time sensitive, and may require an urgent response.

- *Who the message is for*: Ensure the person gets the message by giving it to them or leaving it in a place where they will find it.

- *Contact name and details*: Write down the name of the person leaving the message, and how to get back to them with a response.

An operative taking notes during a phone call

UNACCEPTABLE COMMUNICATION

When communicating, it is very important to stay calm. Think about what you are going to say. An angry word will often encourage an angry response. However, keeping calm and composed will often diffuse a stressful situation. A shouting match rarely ends with a good or productive result.

There are several types of communication that are unacceptable and could result in unemployment. Unacceptable communication includes:

- aggressive communication such as swearing or using inappropriate hand gestures

- racist or sexist comments or gestures

- showing prejudice against people with disabilities.

This type of behaviour shows a lack of respect for others and does not create a safe or pleasant working environment. It will also give your company a poor image if customers see or hear this behaviour. Acting in this way is likely to result in trouble for you and your employer and could even result in a **tribunal** and loss of employment.

Tribunal

A judgement made in court

KNOWLEDGE OF THE CONSTRUCTION INDUSTRY AND BUILT ENVIRONMENT

Buildings come in a wide variety of types in relation to appearance and methods of construction. Despite the variety of buildings, they all have design features in common. In this section we will discuss various parts of buildings and their purpose.

We will also discuss sustainable construction – how buildings can be designed to sit better within the environment, with lower pollution levels and energy requirements both during the building process and when in use.

A house with solar panels

FOUNDATIONS

Foundations serve as a good base on which to put the building. They need to be capable of carrying the weight of the building and any further load that may be put upon it. These are known as **dead loads** and **imposed loads**.

Foundations must be designed to resist any potential movement in the ground on which the building will sit. Ground conditions can vary widely. Soil samples are taken to help decide on the type of foundation to use. This usually takes the form of bore holes dug or drilled around the site. These samples are sent away for testing in a laboratory. The results will identify:

- the soil condition (clay or sandy)
- the depth of the soil
- the depth of the water table
- if any contaminations are present.

The soil condition is important: clay soil drains poorly and can move if it gets waterlogged or dries out completely. Sandy soils drain very well, but can become unstable. A foundation that is suitable for the ground type and load of the building will be designed.

Foundation

Used to spread the load of a building to the subsoil

Dead load

The weight of all the materials used to construct the building

Imposed load

Additional loads that may be placed on the structure, eg people, furniture, wind and snow

INDUSTRY TIP

The type of foundation to be used will usually be decided by the architect and a structural engineer and will be the result of tests.

TYPES OF FOUNDATION

Different types of structures, such as detached houses, high-rise and low-rise buildings, will all require different types of foundation.

High-rise building

Low-rise building

Detached house

STRIP FOUNDATIONS

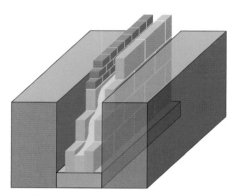

Traditional strip foundation

A strip foundation is the traditional type of foundation used for residential developments (ordinary houses). It is formed by digging a trench to the required width and depth as determined by the soil conditions and the weight of the structure. It is either filled with concrete or a layer of concrete is poured into the bottom. This layer must be a minimum of 150mm thick and is commonly 225mm thick.

Footings are brought up to the level of the **damp proof course** (DPC) using concrete blocks or bricks. These are set out from the centre of the strip of concrete in order to spread the weight evenly. A variety of specialist bricks and blocks are used for this purpose. They need to be able to resist water penetration and therefore frost damage.

Footings

The substructure below ground level. These are projecting courses at the base of a wall

Damp proof course (DPC)

A layer of plastic that prevents damp rising up through a wall needs to be positioned at least 150mm above ground level

Engineering brick

Trench block

It can be economical to fill the trench up to the top with concrete rather than build a substructure – this is known as trench fill. Sometimes it is necessary to build on the edge of the concrete – this is known as an eccentric foundation.

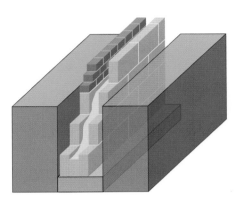

Eccentric foundation

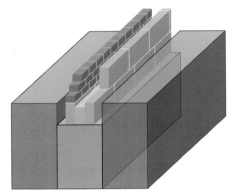

Trench fill foundation

WIDE STRIP FOUNDATIONS

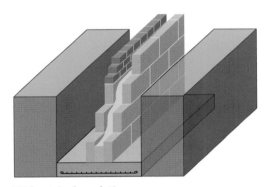

Wide strip foundation

A wide strip foundation is very similar to strip foundation in most of its aspects. The main difference between the two is that a wide strip foundation has steel reinforcements placed within the concrete. The steel gives considerably more strength to the foundation and enables greater loads to be placed on it. Without the steel reinforcements the foundation would need to be much deeper and would need vast amounts of concrete.

PAD FOUNDATIONS

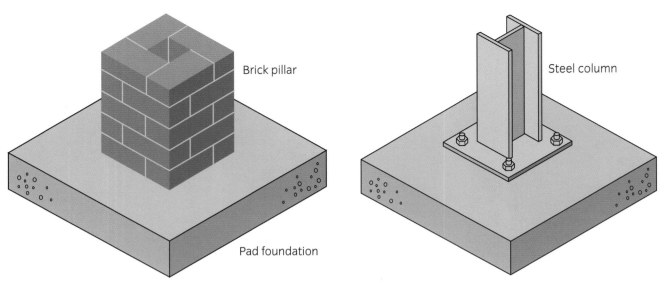

Brick pillar

Pad foundation

Steel column

Pad foundation

Pad foundation with bolts

A pad foundation is used to support a point load such as a column in a steel-framed building. This type of foundation often has bolts set into the top ready for fixing the steel.

INDUSTRY TIP

Foundations are made from concrete. Concrete is made from fine and coarse aggregate (crushed stone) and cement mixed with water. Water reacts with the cement causing it to harden and lock the aggregates together. Concrete is very strong under compression (when weight is put upon it) but is weak when it is pulled (put under tension); therefore steel rods are cast into it to make it stronger.

PILE FOUNDATIONS

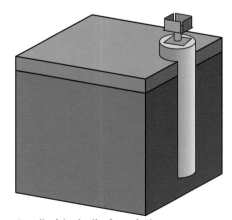

A cylindrical pile foundation

Friction

Resistance between the surface of the concrete foundation and the soil around it

Deep piles are used to transfer the load through unsuitable soil layers into the harder layers of ground below, even down to rock if required (known as end bearing). Some piles use **friction** to provide support. This is known as skin friction. Tall buildings (and especially narrow buildings such as chimneys or towers) have large lateral forces due to side winds and pile foundations resist these forces well.

RAFT FOUNDATIONS

A raft foundation is often laid over an area of softer soil that would be unsuitable for a strip foundation. A raft foundation is a slab of concrete covering the entire base of the building; it spreads the weight of the building over a wider area but still maintains a deeper base around the load-bearing walls.

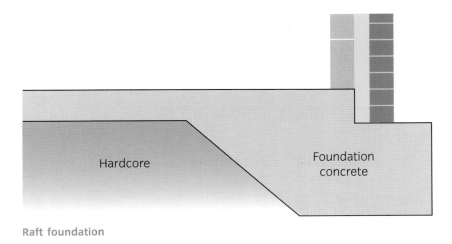

Hardcore

Foundation concrete

Raft foundation

FLOORS

Floors can be divided into two main categories:

- ground floors

- upper floors.

Floors are required to be load-bearing, and there is a wide variety of construction methods depending on the type of building and potential load that will be imposed upon the floor. Floors also may need to prevent:

- heat loss

- transfer of sound

- moisture penetration.

GROUND FLOORS

These may be either solid ground floors or suspended floors.

SOLID FLOORS

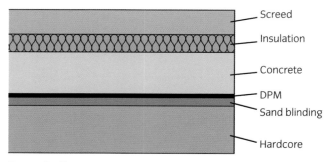

Screed
Insulation
Concrete
DPM
Sand blinding
Hardcore

Concrete floor

Solid concrete floors are laid upon **hardcore** and have a **damp proof membrane** (DPM) built into them to prevent damp coming up through the floor. **Insulation** is also laid into the floor to reduce heat loss. It is important that the insulation is not affected by the high water content of the wet concrete when being poured.

Steel reinforcement can also be used within the concrete to increase strength and reduce cracks.

Hardcore

A mixture of crushed stone and sand laid and compacted to give a good base for the concrete

Damp proof membrane (DPM)

An impermeable layer that prevents damp coming up through the floor. A layer of sand known as blinding is placed below the DPM to prevent any sharp stones below piercing the membrane when the concrete is poured

Insulation

Materials used to retain heat and improve the thermal value of a building; may also be used for managing sound transfer

HOLLOW AND SUSPENDED FLOORS

Upper floors, and some ground floors, are suspended or hollow meaning that instead of resting on the ground beneath, the load is transferred via beams to the walls. Two types of beam used are Posi-Joist and I-beam. Timber joists are usually covered with either chip board or solid timber floor boards.

Concrete with steel reinforcement

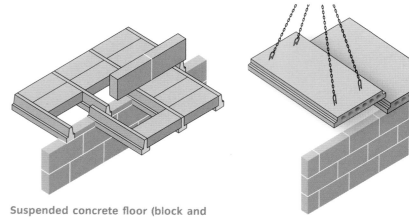

Suspended concrete floor (block and beam)

Precast floor

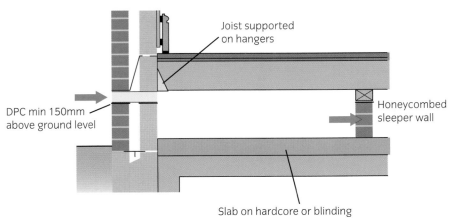

DPC min 150mm above ground level

Joist supported on hangers

Honeycombed sleeper wall

Slab on hardcore or blinding

Suspended wood floor

Posi-Joist

I-beam

UPPER FLOORS

In most domestic dwellings timber floor joists are used following the same principle as timber ground floors, while in large commercial and industrial buildings solid concrete floors are used.

WALLS

Walling for a building can usually be divided in two categories:

- external
- internal.

Walling can be load or non-load-bearing. Load-bearing walls carry the weight of the floors and roof and transfer this weight down to the foundations. A non-load-bearing wall carries no weight.

Lintel

A horizontal member for spanning an opening to support the structure above

Bond

The arrangement or pattern of laying bricks and blocks to spread the load through the wall, also for strength and appearance

Solid wall

Walls of a thickness of one brick and greater

Cavity wall

Walling built in two separate skins (usually of different materials) with a void held together by wall ties

INDUSTRY TIP

Remember, cement will give chemical burns so use the correct PPE while using and mixing it.

ACTIVITY

What are the walls in the building you are sitting in made from? Why do you think these materials were chosen? What are the advantages or disadvantages of these materials?

Walls often have openings in them, eg doors and windows, which will weaken them if they are not constructed correctly. Openings require support (via a **lintel** or arch) across the top to give the wall support and **bond** it together.

EXTERNAL WALLING

External walls need to:

- keep the elements (wind and rain) out of the building
- look good
- fit into the surrounding landscape.

Several methods of construction are used for external walling. Common construction methods are:

- **solid wall**
- **cavity wall**
- timber framing.

SOLID WALLS

Solid wall

Many older traditional buildings have solid walls made from brick, block or stone: see the following table. Solid walls have the disadvantage of being more easily penetrated by damp. Older solid walls are often upgraded by having insulating and waterproofing layers applied to the outside of the wall.

Material used	Description
Bricks 	A very traditional building material made from fired clay, calcium-silicate or concrete. A standard sized brick is 215mm × 102.5mm × 65mm.
Blocks 	These are made of either concrete (crushed stone and cement) or a light-weight cement mixture. They are much bigger than a brick, and are available in various sizes. The most commonly used size is 440mm × 215mm × 100mm. Wider blocks are used for walls where a higher strength or improved sound insulation is required.
Stone 	A natural building material, which varies widely in use and appearance from area to area. Stone may be cut to a uniform size before use or used in its quarried state.
Mortar 	This is used between bricks, blocks and stones to bind them together and increase the strength of the wall. It is a mixture of soft sand and cement mixed with water and other additives if required, eg **plasticiser**, colouring or **lime**. It is important that the strength of the mortar is correct for the type of material that is being used to construct the wall. If the mortar has too much cement in the mix it will be so strong it will not allow movement in the walling due to settlement, and the bricks could crack resulting in the wall needing to be rebuilt. Mortars are mixed to a ratio of materials, eg 1:6. The first number is the proportion of cement with the second being the proportion of sand. A typical mix ratio for masonry walling is 1:5.

Plasticiser

An additive that is used to make the mortar more pliable and easier to work with

Lime

A fine powdered material traditionally used in mortar

CAVITY WALLS

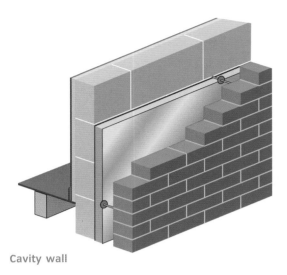

Cavity wall

ACTIVITY

State the minimum performance standards required to meet current building regulations.

ACTIVITY

Find out the current minimum width of cavity allowed.

Leaves

The two walls or skins that make up a cavity wall to comply with current building regulations

Building regulations

A series of documents that set out legal requirements for the standards of building work

The most common type of external walling used today is cavity wall construction.

Cavity walls are two masonry walls built side by side to form an inner and outer leaf (sometimes called skins). The **leaves** are held together with wall ties. These ties are made from rust- and rot-proof material and are built in as the walls are being constructed. The cavity is partially filled with insulation (typically fibreglass batts or polystyrene boards) as required by the **building regulations**. This reduces heat loss and saves energy.

The inner leaf usually carries any loads from the roof and floors down to the foundations and has a decorative finish on the inside, typically plaster which is either painted or papered. The outer leaf resists the elements and protects the inside of the building.

TIMBER FRAMING

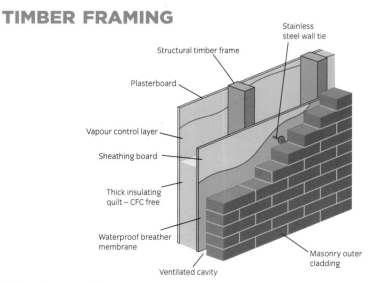

Stainless steel wall tie

Structural timber frame

Plasterboard

Vapour control layer

Sheathing board

Thick insulating quilt – CFC free

Waterproof breather membrane

Ventilated cavity

Masonry outer cladding

Timber frame wall

Timber framing is both a traditional and modern method of building. Traditional buildings using timber framing were made mostly from oak with various in-fills such as brick or plaster to form the walls. Modern timber frame homes are generally built from softwood and have an outer skin of masonry or are clad with timber or plaster to waterproof the structure. Oak framing, as a traditional building method, is becoming increasingly popular again.

Elizabethan oak frame

PREFABRICATED WALLS

Prefabricated wall panel

There are a variety of prefabricated products available, generally made in a factory and then transported to site to be erected. These products enable quick and easy building. Often the **services** are pre-installed.

Services

Those provided by the utility companies, eg gas, electric and water

INTERNAL WALLING

Internal walling can be load or non-load-bearing. Internal partitions divide large internal spaces into smaller rooms.

Internal partitions can be made from studwork or masonry. Studwork partitions consist of studs (which can be made from timber or metal) covered with a sheet material (usually plasterboard).

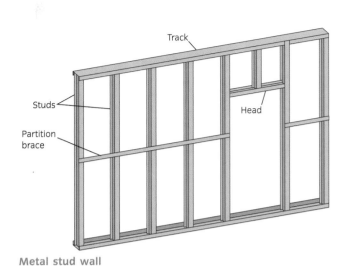

Metal stud wall

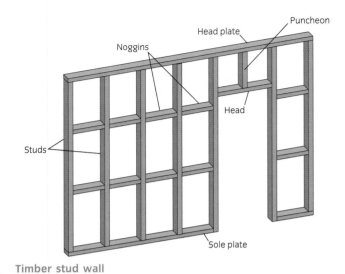

Timber stud wall

WALL FINISHES

External walls made from brick usually have no further finishes added while walls made from blocks are rendered. This is a covering of sand and cement mortar which is then finished with masonry paint.

Internal walls are most often plastered with a thin layer of gypsum plaster over plasterboard; this gives a very smooth hardwearing finish which is then usually finished with emulsion paint or papered coverings.

It is important to **size** new plaster to give a good base before applying further coverings of paint or paper coverings. This first coat of paint or paste is usually thinned down by 10% with clean water.

INDUSTRY TIP

At least two coats of emulsion are usually required for new plaster.

Size

To apply a watered-down or mist-coat of paint or paste to new plaster

ROOFS

Roofs are designed to protect the structure below by keeping the weather out. As heat rises, the roof must be well insulated to prevent heat loss and improve the energy efficiency of the building.

TYPES OF ROOFS

Roofs come in a wide variety of designs as the following pictures show.

Pitched roof

Flat roof

ROOF COMPONENTS

Roofs are commonly covered with slates or tiles. Slates are a natural product. Slate is a type of mineral that can be split into thin sheets. Artificial cement fibre slates are also available. Tiles can be made from clay or concrete.

Slate

Cement fibre slate

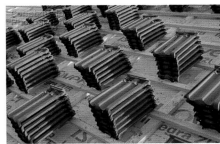

Roof tiles

A felt is laid below the roofing material to provide additional protection in case some water gets through the tiles.

Flashings are commonly made from lead and are used to provide waterproofing at joints where roofing materials meet walls and around chimneys.

Flashing providing waterproofing

Flashing around a chimney

SERVICES

Buildings contain services such as:

- water

- electricity

- gas supplies.

Additionally, waste such as sewage and water run-off have to be considered.

WATER

Water is brought into a building using pipes. Supply pipes used are usually made of plastic, with internal domestic plumbing being made from plastic or copper. Plumbing is installed using a variety of fittings including tees, elbows and reducers. Bathrooms, kitchens and most heating systems require plumbing.

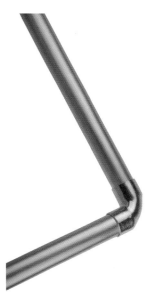

Copper pipe

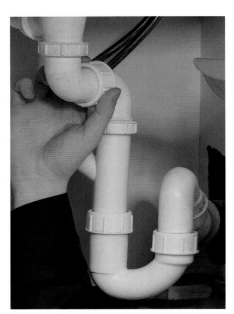

Plastic waste water pipe

Pipe fittings: Tee (left), elbow (middle) and reducer (right)

Not only is water carried into a building, it is also taken away. Rainwater run-off is collected into gutters and taken away via downpipes and drains and returned to the ground or stored for later use.

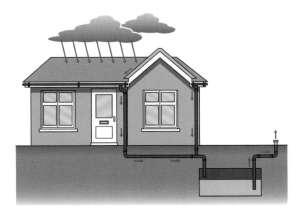

Rainwater gutter flowing down pipes and into drain

SEWAGE

Sewage is taken away from the building via drains and is disposed of either into a sewer or into a septic tank/sewage treatment plant.

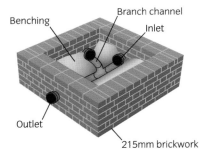

Benching   Branch channel
Inlet
Outlet
215mm brickwork

Benched drain

Septic tank

Sewage treatment plant

ELECTRICITY

Electricity is an important service provided to buildings. It powers lighting and heating. It is brought into a building through cables.

Electricity cables, switches and socket

Pipework to boiler

ACTIVITY

What services are being used in the building you are sitting in? How are they brought into the building?

GAS

Gas is brought into a building using pipes. Gas powers heating systems and provides fuel for cooking.

OTHER SERVICES

Other services that are installed include telephone systems and other data cables for broadband and entertainment systems.

SUSTAINABILITY

Our planet is a fixed size. Fossil fuels, eg oil and coal, that we take from the ground are not infinite, ie they will run out one day. However, the wind, the sun and the tides will always be there. These are sustainable sources of energy.

Building materials can be sustainable if they are chosen carefully. For example, the process of manufacturing concrete uses a lot of fuel and produces a lot of carbon dioxide (a gas that some say is damaging the climate).

On the other hand, trees absorb carbon dioxide as they grow, look nice and the timber they produce is an excellent building material. However, some timber is harvested from rainforests without thought for the surrounding environment or are harvested to such an extent that certain species are close to extinction. Managed forests where trees are replanted after harvesting provide a sustainable source of timber.

Here are some questions to consider regarding sustainability in construction.

MATERIALS

- How far have the materials been brought? Locally sourced materials do not have to be transported far, thus reducing fuel use.

- Are the materials sustainably sourced? Has the timber come from a managed forest or has it come from a rainforest with no regard to the environment?

- Have the materials been manufactured with the minimum of energy and waste?

DESIGN

Is there an alternative design that can be used that uses more sustainable materials? For example, a timber frame instead of concrete block or brick.

The table below shows some sustainable materials.

Material	Image
Straw bales	
Cob (soil)	
Timber	Redwood Spruce Oak
Bamboo	

ENERGY EFFICIENCY

Energy is expensive and is only going to get more expensive. As the population increases more and more energy will be required. This needs to come from somewhere and its production can be damaging to the environment. The less power a building uses the better and if it can produce its own that is a bonus. Energy-saving measures can save a lot of power consumption.

INSULATION

Light, air-filled materials tend to have better thermal insulation properties than heavy, dense materials. This means that heat cannot easily pass from one side to another and so if these materials are used in a building it will require less heating during the winter and will remain cooler during the summer.

The following drawing shows how much heat a typical home loses through different parts of the property. Better insulation will reduce the amount of heat lost.

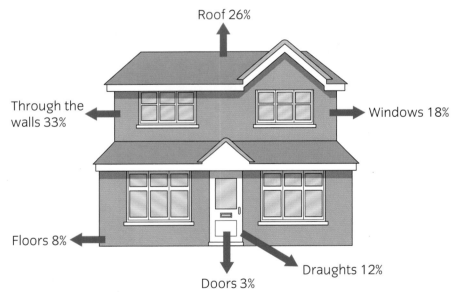

Sources of heat loss from a house

OUR HOUSE

What insulation has been used in the building you are sitting in? Is the building energy efficient? Is it cold? Does it take a lot of heating? Take a look at 'Our House' and identify the insulation measures used there.

The table below shows some examples of insulation.

Type of insulation	Description
Blue jean and lambswool	Lambswool is a natural insulator. Blue jean insulation comes from recycled denim.
Fibreglass/Rockwool™	This is made from glass, often from old recycled bottles or mineral wool. It holds a lot of air within it and therefore is an excellent insulator. It is also cheap to produce. It does however use up a fair bit of room as it takes a good thickness to comply with building regulations. Similar products include plastic fibre insulation made from plastic bottles and lambswool.
PIR (polyisocyanurate)	This is a solid insulation with foil layers on the faces. It is lightweight, rigid and easy to cut and fit. It has excellent insulation properties. Polystyrene is similar to PIR. Although polystyrene is cheaper, its thermal properties are not as good.
Multifoil	A modern type of insulation made up of many layers of foil and thin insulation layers. These work by reflecting heat back into the building. Usually used in conjunction with other types of insulation.
Double glazing and draught proofing measures	The elimination of draughts and air flows reduces heat loss and improves efficiency.

MAKING BETTER USE OF EXISTING AND FREE ENERGY

SOLAR POWER

The sun always shines and during the day its light reaches the ground (even on cloudy days). This energy can be used. A simple use of this is to allow sunlight to enter a building. With a little thought in design, light can reach deep into a building via roof lights and light tunnels. This means that internal artificial lighting requirements are reduced, therefore saving energy.

Solar panels can generate hot water or electricity, and once the cost of installation has been covered the energy they produce is totally free.

Solar panel

A panel that absorbs sun rays to generate electricity or hot water

Solar panels

HEAT SOURCE AND RECOVERY

Humans give off a fair bit of energy as they go through a normal day (eg body heat, heat given off by hairdryers, cookers, refrigerators and other activities) and this can be conserved. Modern air-conditioning systems take the heat from stale air and put it into the fresh air coming in.

Heat can be taken from the ground and even the air outside.

WIND POWER

Wind power is becoming more widespread. However some people feel that wind turbines are damaging the visual environment as they spoil the appearance of the countryside. Individuals will have their own opinion on whether wind power is a good thing or not as there are many considerations to be taken into account.

Wind turbine

WATER POWER

Water is another source of power, whether that be hydro-electric (water from dams turning turbines) or wave power, which is currently under development.

BIOMASS HEATING

Biomass heating (using wood and other non-fossil fuels) is also becoming more popular as these systems can heat water efficiently as well as heat rooms, and of course a well-insulated building does not require a lot of heating.

ENERGY-EFFICIENT GOODS AND APPLIANCES

Energy-efficient electrical goods (eg low-energy light bulbs) and appliances (eg dishwashers, fridges and washing machines) which use a reduced amount of power and less water are available.

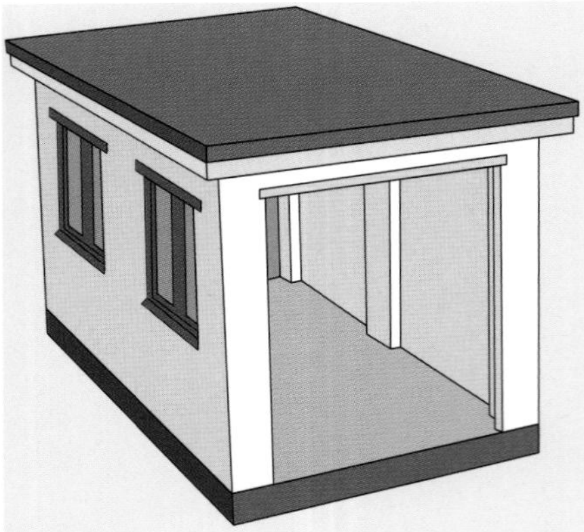

Case Study: Kayleigh

Kayleigh is to build a small single garage at the rear of a house. It must be big enough to accommodate an estate car and give enough room to allow the user to get out and walk around the car. The garage has two windows, an up-and-over door at the front and a flat roof. She has been asked to provide a plan of this garage for the client.

Draw this garage to a scale that will fit onto an A4 piece of paper. Include the window openings, the door, the thickness of the walls (which will be single block) and the piers.

Work through the following questions to check your learning.

1 What is the perimeter of this room?

Side 1: **2.5m**
Side 2: **5m**

a 5m.

b 7m.

c 15m.

d 17m.

2 A message that is passed on by word of mouth rather than in writing is

a open to interpretation

b very accurate

c easy to understand if shouted

d easily remembered.

3 What is a component drawing?

a A plan of the whole building, floor by floor.

b A section through a part of the structure.

c An elevation of the walls.

d A detail in a room.

4 What is the foundation type shown?

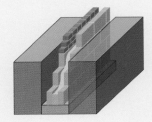

a Strip.

b Pile.

c Raft.

d Pad.

5 What is the foundation type shown?

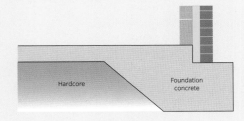

Hardcore   Foundation concrete

a Strip.

b Pile.

c Raft.

d Pad.

6 What is the component shown?

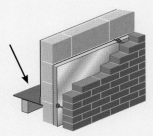

a Damp proof membrane.

b Strip foundation.

c Damp proof course.

d Raft foundation.

7 Which one of the following materials has the **best** thermal insulation properties?

a Brick.

b Concrete.

c Glass.

d Polystyrene.

8 Concrete sets because it contains

a aggregate

b sand

c hardcore

d cement.

9 A flat roof has a pitch of less than

    a 8°

    b 10°

    c 12°

    d 15°.

10 Load-bearing walls transmit weight down to the

    a foundations

    b floors

    c roof

    d windows.

Chapter 3
Unit 121: Prepare background surfaces and mix plastering materials

Building methods and materials are always evolving, with many changes to the way we work and the practices we use. Modern materials have been developed and manufactured to improve the efficiency of mixing plaster and to ensure compatibility with different backgrounds, simplifying the plastering process. Despite this, over time surfaces can break down due to age, poor surface preparation or bad workmanship (including poor mixing). These surfaces then need to be restored to bring them back to their original state.

By reading this chapter you will know how to:

1 Prepare background surfaces.
2 Prepare for mixing plastering materials.
3 Mix plastering materials.

PREPARE BACKGROUND SURFACES

Building out

Applying plaster to a very uneven background surface until it has an even surface

Adhere/adhesion

How well plaster sticks or grips to the background

Suction

The rate at which a background absorbs moisture

Key

How rough or smooth a background surface is. Creating a rough surface on a background helps the plaster adhere to it

The key to creating a good plaster surface is identifying and preparing the background properly before starting work. It is important to understand that not all backgrounds have the same properties. Some will be soft and weak, some will be hard and dense, and some will be uneven and require '**building out**'.

Different backgrounds need to be prepared for plastering in different ways. There are several steps that you need to follow to make sure the plaster **adheres** well to the surface. These steps include controlling the **suction** and ensuring that the background has a good **key**. Only then can you apply the plaster.

Checking the suction will tell you if the background is dry and porous. You can do this by splashing water onto the background with a brush. The quicker the water is absorbed, the higher the background's suction.

Testing a background's suction by splashing it with water

- No suction or low suction (when the splashed water stays on the background's surface) will indicate that the background is hard or dense.

- High-suction backgrounds (when the splashed water soaks in quickly) will absorb moisture from the plaster mix and may cause it to dry too quickly when applied.

TYPES OF BACKGROUND SURFACES

Let's examine the surface characteristics of different backgrounds in more detail.

Type of background	Comment
Hollow and solid blocks 	Newly constructed buildings that have block walling need little preparation before you apply plaster to their surface because they have medium to adequate key. The surface is flat and can be plastered using traditional or modern pre-mixed plasters. Block walling built to today's specifications and standards needs only a backing coat and finish, known as 'float and set'.
Lightweight aerated blocks 	These blocks are lightweight and weak with an adequate key, but have high suction levels. Cement-based mixes are not compatible with these backgrounds because they are too strong for this surface. This type of block is best suited for pre-mixed plasters that are weaker than the background. Applying a solution of PVA (polyvinyl acetate) diluted with water (to the manufacturer's instructions) will seal the surface and control the suction.
Plasterboard and fixings 	There are several different types of plasterboard, but they are all made with a plaster core within an outer skin of paper. Plasterboard may have square or tapered edges. Before applying plaster, both types need to be reinforced at their joints in order to prevent cracking. Plasterboard has a flat surface with low suction and only requires a finish coat, applied using a one-coat system that consists of two layers of plaster at an average thickness of 3mm.
	Plasterboard can be fixed using galvanised nails or dry wall screws. The fixings should be flush or they can penetrate the paper skin surface of the board. Fixing plasterboard over uneven timber studwork may require **filling out**; this should be done with a bonding-grade plaster that contains the aggregate **vermiculite**.
	Avoid using plasterboard in damp areas as this will cause the core of the board to perish and become weak. You will learn more about plasterboard in Chapter 5.

Filling out

Applying plaster to uneven areas to form a straight background

Vermiculite

A lightweight aggregate added to pre-mixed lightweight plaster to improve its bonding capabilities

Type of background	Comment
Lath backgrounds 	Laths were traditionally used on timber backgrounds. They consist of thin strips of wood over which plaster can be spread. It can be a time-consuming process to prepare, fix and plaster this surface. This type of background is still used in the restoration of listed buildings.
Existing solid plaster 	This type of surface is common with solid walls that require a makeover due to poor surface condition that has developed over the years. Over skim makeovers enhance the appearance of a wall by re-skimming the surface without removing the old plaster from the background.
	When applying plaster to this type of surface, remember that it can only be as good as the background you plaster over. The surface needs to be solid and sound with no hollowness. Any flaking paint and surface grime or grease that could prevent the new plaster from **bonding** should be removed.
	This background has no key and if it is painted usually no suction, unless the background has different properties that are hidden behind the decorated wall surface. For example, if the wall has been re-plastered after having electrical services installed, it may contain different plasters on the background, creating different suction rates.
	This background will need a bonding adhesive on its surface before it can be re-plastered. You will learn about bonding adhesives later on in this chapter.
Existing plaster surface that has decayed over time 	There are many different types of plaster surface that may need to be replaced or restored, whether due to poor workmanship or deterioration over time. This type of surface may show signs of cracking, hollowness or a crumbling surface that cannot be decorated due to its condition. You will have to remove any existing surface finish before you are able to identify its background properties.

Bonding

When the plaster sufficiently adheres to the background surface

INDUSTRY TIP

You can check a background for hollowness by tapping its surface.

Type of background	Comment
Clay bricks 	Clay bricks were very popular at one time and can be found in all types of buildings. A common fault with clay bricks is that they would shell their face, causing the plaster to 'blow' (come away from the background). This type of background is often uneven due to the fact that the bricks were manufactured in kilns at great heat which made them all a slightly different shape. They were then laid on a lime mortar bed, which is very weak in strength. Clay bricks and lime mortar joints have a high absorption rate that will cause high suction levels. This surface will need to be treated with a bonding adhesive before plastering. Raking out the joints will also improve the key.
Concrete common bricks 	These bricks are made from coarse aggregate mixed with cement. This surface is smooth and hard which means the key is poor and the suction is minimal. A bonding slurry is best suited for this surface. You can read about bonding slurry mixes further on in this chapter (see pages 115–117).
Concrete surface 	This is a hard dense surface with poor key; it may have absorption, and it needs to be scabbled if smooth. It will need preparing with a slurry. If using sand and cement, any slurry will need to be applied to the surface to bond. However, lightweight bonding plaster adheres well without preparing the background.
Engineering bricks 	This is a hard, dense surface with poor key and no absorption rate. The face of the brick has a glossy surface that makes it difficult to prepare for plastering. It has an enamel look and no suction. This surface needs to be **scabbled** or roughened to remove the sheen. You can then **slurry** the surface with a bonding adhesive (see page 115). Alternatively, you can fix sheets of **EML** (expanded metal lathing) to its surface with mechanical fixings – this is a good way to reinforce and form a key on the background.

Scabbling

The removal of the surface finish by mechanical means, producing a suitable key

Slurry

A thin, sloppy cement applied to backgrounds in order to bond plaster to its surface

EML

Sheet material in the form of diamond-shaped mesh that is used to reinforce a surface. This material can be fixed with screws and plugs, galvanised nails or it can be bedded into the plaster material

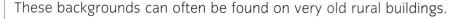

Type of background	Comment
Stone and slate backgrounds 	These backgrounds can often be found on very old rural buildings. Stone can have rough or smooth surfaces. Due to their irregular shape and size, this background is very uneven and will require additional layers in order to build out the surface, the first layer being the **dubbing out** coat. Slate is similar to stone in that it can have uneven surfaces with a smooth face and no suction. The mortar joints between the slate and stone can be very thick and wide, causing large voids. The old mortar joints will need to be filled in with a suitable plaster mix after being raked out, then keyed with a comb scratcher. Any large stone or slate that has a smooth surface will need to be prepared with a bonding slurry (see page 115) to improve the bond.
Concrete lintels and pad stones 	This surface is generally flat and hard with minimal suction. Concrete is used to make lintels and pad stones, which provide load-bearing surfaces above openings such as windows. Again if using traditional sand and cement, this surface should be keyed and slurried, unless a lightweight bonding plaster is used.
Timber wall plates covered with EML 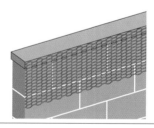	This background generally has low suction and no key. Timber can move and twist with moisture contact. Wall plates are used on top of walls as a fixing for the roof trusses. EML is a good way of reinforcing the timber and providing a key.
Composite backgrounds 	Backgrounds that are made up of two or more different materials. One method of preparing this type of background is to fix EML mechanically to the surface. This will strengthen and reinforce the background and the applied plaster.

Dubbing out

Filling out between uneven surfaces such as stone joints, building up the uneven surface until it is smooth

REMOVING EXISTING PLASTER AND CLEANING DOWN SURFACES

Removing old plaster from backgrounds is a process known as 'hacking'. It is important to remove all loose plaster from the surface. This can be carried out by hand or mechanically using various tools and equipment, but before you start you need to protect certain areas to prevent damage that can be caused by this type of work.

Plywood sheeting can be used to protect floors and openings such as windows and doors. Dust sheets and tarpaulins are good for protecting furniture that might be too heavy to move out of the building. Causing damage to the client's property is unprofessional and can be costly to replace!

Hacking a surface

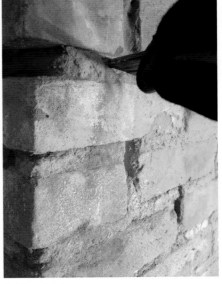

Raking joints

When you carry out this type of work, you need to be aware of the risks caused by high dust levels and the build-up of debris. Building sites can be dangerous places with many hidden hazards. Reading the risk assessments will make you aware of the hazards involved with this type of work and identify the type of personal protective equipment (PPE) that you need to wear. You also need to follow the method statement, which will give you a safe means of work. For more information on risk assessments and method statements, see Chapter 1, pages 5–6.

It is important to dispose of the loose rubble removed from the surface before it builds up around you. Using a shovel, brush and wheelbarrow is a good way of removing and transporting your rubble – using a wheelbarrow will be less strenuous on your body than using buckets and will reduce the risk of injury.

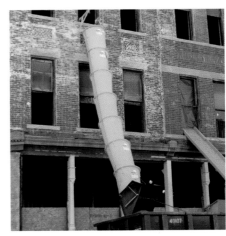

A chute leading to a skip

Housekeeping

Making sure that your work area is kept safe and tidy

If you are hacking surfaces on different levels in a building, a good way to safely get rid of rubble is to put it down a chute. This can be connected to the skip. Good **housekeeping** will help ensure a safe and efficient work area.

TOOLS AND EQUIPMENT

Hand tools

There are several types of hand tools that can be used to hack and remove old plaster. This type of work can take a long time to complete. Making sure that you have the correct tools can make the job so much easier.

Try to get into the habit of maintaining all your hand tools. When you have finished using your hand tools at the end of the day, put them away carefully to prevent them getting damaged or lost.

These tools are covered by PUWER – see Chapter 1, pages 16–17 for more information on these regulations. Ensure you wear appropriate PPE when using the tools, and that you have been trained how to use the tools safely.

An old chisel with a flattened mushroom head should not be used

A safe-to-use chisel without a mushroom head

Tool	Use
Lump hammer 	Lump hammers are made with timber, steel or fibreglass shafts (handles) that are inserted into a rectangular head with a flat face made from cast iron. Its purpose, like any hammer, is to cause impact, knocking against the head of the bolster to remove old plaster from backgrounds. It is also known as a club hammer.
Bolster chisel	There are different types of bolsters used for removing plaster, with various widths of blades. The safer and better ones will have a rubber hand-protector at the head. Bolsters with mushroom heads should not be used as these may chip off and cause injury when in use.

Tool	Use
Scutch hammer	This hammer has sharp teeth and can be used for removing plaster. It leaves a rough surface on backgrounds.
Pointing hammer	This hammer has a flat end on one side and a pointed end on the other. It is a good tool for getting in between thin, tight surfaces like brick and stone to rake out the joints. It is also known as a pick hammer.
Claw hammer	This hammer is used when preparing timber backgrounds that have been previously plastered. Its main function is to remove old nails that might be left in the timber surface, or to remove old lath work or damaged plasterboard.
Lath hammer	A traditional tool used by plasterers, before plasterboard was widely used, to cut wooden laths when lathing. Also used for hacking off old sand–lime plaster from walls.
Crow bar	This is a long bar that can be used to lever materials that are wedged in place. It can also be used to remove stubborn nails and screws.

ACTIVITY

List the tools and PPE required to remove a lime mortar plastered surface from a solid background.

Tool	Use
Wire brush 	This is a good tool for cleaning the face of backgrounds that still contain old dry plaster or flaking paint.
Wire brush attachment	This can be fitted to a power drill to remove paint and expose the background surface.

Power tools

INDUSTRY TIP

All electrical power tools on site need to be run on the recommended voltage of 110 volts. You can step down the voltage from 230V to 110V using a transformer; this will make it safer to use.

A mechanical breaker

Mechanical 'breakers' are far more efficient than hand tools and can remove plaster surfaces with ease. A breaker is a heavy-duty power tool generally used on hard, stubborn areas that are difficult to remove by hand using just a hammer and bolster.

Power tool safety

All electrical tools and equipment need to be checked before use. They should be well maintained and carry a PAT (portable appliance test) sticker to confirm that they are safe to use. (See Chapter 1, page 37 for more about PAT tests, including an example of a PAT sticker.)

Mechanical breakers are very heavy and noisy when in use. Care must be taken when using this type of tool. They can also cause an injury called 'vibration white finger' (VWS), which is caused by the continuous vibration of the tools in the hands. As well as fingers changing colour, fingers can become numb or tingle and lose strength. It is recommended that mechanical breakers are used for short periods of time only, as determined by a risk assessment or method statement (for more information see Chapter 1, pages 5–6). You should take regular intervals and wear the correct PPE. Modern tools are equipped with special anti-vibration dampers and there are specially designed gloves with extra vibration padding. These measures help reduce the risk of vibration white finger.

The Control of Vibration at Work Regulations 2005, created under the Health and Safety at Work Act (HASAWA) 1974, is the legislation in the UK that governs exposure to vibration and aims to prevent **HAVS** from occurring.

Setting up and using a mechanical breaker
Before you use a mechanical breaker, you need to consider several factors that will help you carry out your work safely and efficiently. You must be aware of the risks involved with using power tools, including:

- risk of electric shock

- exposure to dust

- high noise levels

- handling and lifting issues.

Referring to the risk assessment before you start work can help prevent accidents. Refer back to Chapter 1 for more information on risk assessments.

You will also need to consider working at height when preparing backgrounds, whether you are working off a standard hop-up (see Chapter 4, page 141), staging or fully erected scaffold. Access platforms must be kept clear of fallen debris to eliminate trip hazards, and signs must be displayed to warn others of the dangers. Falling or flying debris can cause damage not just to your tools, work equipment and the client's property, but also to you, to work colleagues and to the general public. Following the method statement will help avoid this – these clear rules are set out and followed to eliminate hazards.

Before using a mechanical breaker or any other power tool, you must have been trained in how to use it. Your supervisor will show you how to set up the power tool and demonstrate how to use it safely. But there are also other measures to take to make sure your work is safe:

- With your supervisor, check that there are no hidden services behind the plaster. You can do this by looking at the drawing or using a detector like the one pictured. Any hidden services will need to be clearly marked up on the surface of the wall before work starts.

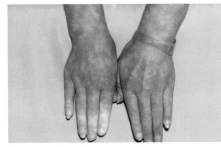
Visible effects of vibration white finger

HAVS
Hand–arm vibration syndrome, an injury caused by using vibrating power tools. Also known as 'vibration white finger'

ACTIVITY
Make a list of the hazards associated with working from access equipment while hacking backgrounds.

A detector

Always wear the correct safety clothing and PPE

A portable dust-extraction unit

- Before you use this type of portable power tool, read the manufacturer's guidelines. These will tell you about how to use the tool safely and the appropriate protective clothing and equipment to use.

- Before you start hacking and removing plaster using a mechanical breaker, adequate dust extraction must be set up in the room to reduce dust levels.

Flying debris and high noise levels are some of the other hazards that you need to be aware of. Due to the dangers involved with this type of work, you will need to cordon off the work area with barriers to prevent any unauthorised person from accessing the area. Clear signs should also be used to warn co-workers and members of the public of the danger.

Any access equipment assembled for the work must be erected by a competent person. You should always adhere to the Work at Heights Regulations 2005 (as amended) when working from access equipment (see Chapter 1, pages 24–30).

CLEANING AND WASTE DISPOSAL

Make sure you have protected the surrounding areas and components before starting work, as removing large amounts of plaster causes lots of waste to build up, especially if you are using a power tool.

Disposing of waste materials to a landfill site can be a costly and time-consuming process. You can help reduce the cost by recycling wherever possible.

Plasterboard and gypsum waste can be collected and processed into gypsum powder, which the plasterboard manufacturers can re-use as raw material to make new plasterboard. Plasterboard and gypsum waste should be sorted and stored separate from other waste.

Cement render waste can be used as low-grade fill or aggregate material. Again, there are environmental and cost advantages associated in doing this rather than dumping it in a landfill site, avoiding the landfill levy or tax.

INDUSTRY TIP

A good method of reducing dust when hacking off is to dampen down the surfaces using water.

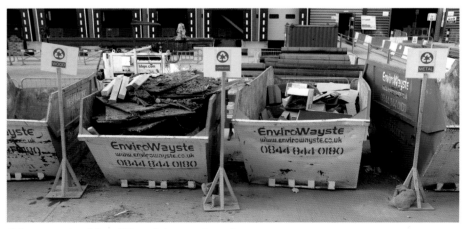

Skips organised for different types of waste

Once the hacking process has been completed and all the loose rubble and debris has been safely cleared, the next stage is to remove any high spots or loose debris that may still exist on the background. This can be done by chipping the surface with a scutch hammer. This is a good tool for this job as it is light to use and has teeth designed to remove small areas of plaster (see page 109).

The remaining dust on the surfaces should be brushed off to leave a clean background.

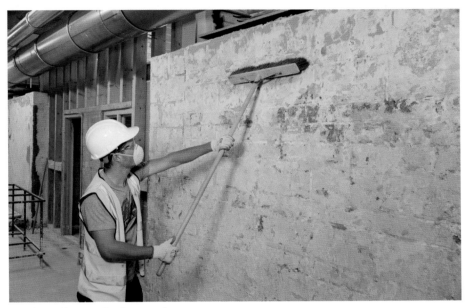

Brushing down a background

FORMING A KEY AND USING BONDING AGENTS

Harder surfaces with poor key need to be prepared using different techniques and materials.

FORMING A KEY

Mechanical key

Mechanical scabbling tools are used on dense smooth surfaces to create a rough area that will result in a good key, increasing its bonding properties. This tool has teeth or pins that are made from strong steel that vibrate on the background surface.

Preparing a concrete surface with a scabbler

Expanded metal lathing (EML)

Another good way of providing a background with reinforcement and key is to fix EML to its surface, especially if the surface contains large cracks or different composite (materials). EML is also used on timber backgrounds, such as old timber lintels and wall plates.

A composite background of brick- and blockwork

Fixed EML to a composite background

You are about to plaster an internal wall of 'Our House' with a lightweight plaster. However, before you can do this you will need to prepare the timber wall plates that are fitted to the perimeter on top of the blockwork. These are used for fixing the roof trusses, too.

1   Make a list of the materials you will use to prepare the timber wall plates.

2   Give details of the manufacturer's website for the materials you will use.

3   Work out the perimeter length and calculate the amount of materials needed.

4   State the reason why you need to prepare the timber before applying plaster with the selected materials.

5   What are the health and safety issues when carrying out the work?

USING BONDING AGENTS

PVA

PVA is the abbreviation for polyvinyl acetate, a water-based glue that is used for preparing background surfaces by improving adhesion.

PVA is mainly used mixed with water for sealing suction. However, if it is used neat it can be used to bond finishing plaster to low-suction backgrounds. When using undercoat plasters, it is advisable to mix the PVA with Ordinary Portland Cement (**OPC**) – this will then become a slurry and a strong **bonding agent** for cement-based plasters.

PVA pre-plastering tests

Below are three pre-plastering tests that you could carry out using PVA.

■   *Test 1*: Sealing a surface. Mix 1 part PVA and 5 parts water. Apply the mix to a brick surface with a brush and leave to dry.

■   *Test 2*: Bonding finishing plaster. Mix 1 part PVA and 2 parts water. Apply the mix on a painted surface. Leave it to go tacky, then mix a little finishing plaster and apply it to the PVA surface.

■   *Test 3*: Bonding cement-based plaster. Mix 1 part PVA with 1 part cement. Paint the mixture onto a small stone surface, then mix some sand and cement and apply this while the surface of the PVA is still tacky.

PVA

OPC

The most commonly used cement in mortar

Bonding agents

Slurry coats used to bond plaster to a background that has poor key

Applying slurry coats

There are two main methods used to apply a slurry coat for bonding cement-based undercoat plasters.

- *Method 1*: Mix and apply the slurry to the background with a brush and then apply plaster direct to the slurry while it is still wet and tacky. This method will bond both surfaces at the same time.

Wet slurry method

- *Method 2*: Mix the dry slurry with water and apply direct to the surface with a brush, then **stipple** the surface to create a textured finish that forms a good key. This type of slurry is left for 24 hours to go hard before cement-based plaster is applied.

Stipple

Creating a rough textured surface to improve adhesion before applying plaster

Dry slurry method

THE CITY & GUILDS TEXTBOOK

There are many new products for bonding plasters on the market today that have been developed in laboratories. For example, ThistleBond-it and Febond Blue Grit have been developed for over skimming solid surfaces. You can apply these adhesives with a soft brush or roller.

A traditional method for bonding surfaces is using a spatterdash slurry. This is a mixture of cement and sharp sand made into a slurry and then thrown onto the background with a paddle or small shovel. Some commercial types of this slurry have glues added to increase and improve the bond.

ThistleBond-it

Febond Blue Grit

The spatterdash method

COMMON PLASTERING FAULTS

Faults occur in plastering work due to a number of factors, including the following:

- Applying plaster onto poorly prepared backgrounds can cause defects in the finished work.

- Plaster applied to background surfaces should be slightly weaker than the background; applying plaster that is stronger than the background will cause stress, causing the plaster to crack and blow.

- Hot and cold climate conditions can affect the set of plasters in different ways. Mixing in freezing conditions will affect the strength quality of the mix and cause the plaster to crumble when set. Hot conditions can remove the moisture content from the mix; this will affect the curing process and can weaken the mix.

INDUSTRY TIP

Over mixing or remixing plastering materials affects the setting process and can lead to slow setting or fast setting.

ACTIVITY

When you're next in the workshop or your workplace, carry out a suction test on various backgrounds to see how fast they absorb moisture. You can do this by splashing them with water using a small brush and seeing how fast the water absorbs into the background.

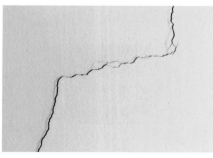

A loose surface

A fine crazing plaster surface

Stock rotation

Making sure that older materials (such as bags of plaster) are at the front and/or top of the stack and so are used first, before their use by date

- Using pre-mixed plaster on persistently damp backgrounds should be avoided. Gypsum is a product that absorbs moisture when set and will perish in these conditions.

- Backgrounds that have poor key and low suction will not bond and will become loose over time.

- Applying plaster onto backgrounds that have high suction levels can cause the plaster to lose its moisture content, weakening its initial strength.

- Plaster applied over high-suction backgrounds will lose its moisture content too quickly and produce a fine crazing surface. This is also known as fire cracking.

PREPARE FOR MIXING PLASTERING MATERIALS

Plastering materials used today include traditional materials and modern pre-mixed lightweight plasters that have been specially developed to be used on a variety of different internal backgrounds. Over the years, plastering materials have become more versatile due to improved setting times and the strength that they provide.

STORAGE

Storing materials for plastering is very important. A clear, flat surface needs to be set out for pallet storage of the plastering materials. The storage area must provide shelter from moisture and frost, as these can affect the shelf life of the materials.

Depending on the storage areas available, materials such as aggregates can be supplied loose, in sacks or in sealed bags. Bagged materials such as plasters, cement and lime are bagged when manufactured and contain a 'use by date' stamp. Stock rotation should be carried out in the storage area with these products. Today's bagged products contain a lot more information than in previous years, including information on mixing, storage and safety.

PLASTERING MATERIALS

Historically, the plastering industry used a mixture of hydraulic lime and coarse sand with horse or goat hair added for reinforcement.

This mix was slow setting, weak and caused many problems such as cracking and poor surface condition. These materials are still used but mainly for **heritage** purposes, which includes restoration and conservation work. Hydrated lime is still common in cement-based mixes and this will be explained later in this chapter.

Heritage

The term used to express the identity, age and history of a building

Conservation plastering using lime plaster

TRADITIONAL MORTAR

As mentioned, coarse sand, hydraulic lime and horse or goat hair are the materials used for making traditional mortar. It is best mixed in a portable or small pan mixer. The animal hair is added to reinforce and bind the plaster mix. This is best added during the mixing process, scattering the hair into the ingredients that make the mix.

A portable mortar pan mixer

CEMENT

Stacked bags of cement

Cement is used to bind and provide strength in the mix. It is made from limestone and clay and is used because of its faster setting time compared with lime mixes. Cement mixed with sand and water will begin to set after 45 minutes and will normally be completely set by the next day.

Cement-based mixes can take several days to reach their final strength. This process is known as 'curing'.

SAND

Sand is an aggregate and must be well-graded when used in a mix. Well-graded means the sand will have a uniform mix of small, medium and large grains that are angular in shape.

Sand

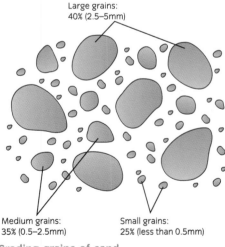

Large grains: 40% (2.5–5mm)

Medium grains: 35% (0.5–2.5mm)

Small grains: 25% (less than 0.5mm)

Grading grains of sand

There are several types of sand.

- *Dredged sand* is most commonly used today in plaster mixes. It is brown or yellow in colour and has been dredged up from the bottom of an **estuary**.

Estuary

Where the mouth of a river or stream meets the sea's tides

- *Pit sand* is quarried from the ground. Red in colour, this sand is generally classed as being too round and fine in grain. However, other types of pit sand, such as Leighton Buzzard sand which is a well-graded coarse sand, are considered suitable for plaster mixes.

- *Coarse sand/crushed aggregate* have large voids of air between grains. However, they can be mixed with finer sand when used in plastering mixes.

- *Sea sand* is not recommended for plastering as it contains salt which can penetrate plastered surfaces in the form of a white powder, known as efflorescence. It can also contain impurities such as shells, and is badly graded.

Sand is used to bulk the mix. Too much **silt** will prevent the cement from binding with the sand and cause the mix to be weak. Sand can be purchased loose, in bags or in sacks. Sand used in plastering mixes should be protected from leaves or animal contamination as these can affect the binding and quality of the surface finish. A good cover or tarpaulin should also be used to protect it from rain water as this can cause **sand bulking**.

LIME

Lime is another material that has many uses in plastering mixes. It is made by crushing limestone and heating it in a kiln. Lime comes in bags and should be stored on a pallet in dry conditions. There are two types used in plastering mixes: hydrated lime and hydraulic lime.

Hydrated lime does not set when added to plastering mixes. However, this has many benefits. Lime added to a cement-based mix will improve the mix's workability and adhesion and help prevent shrinkage. Another benefit of lime is it creates suction.

Hydraulic lime has a 'chemical set' and sets very slowly when mixed with sand. The setting times can be influenced by the temperature – setting will take longer in winter than in the summer, so good planning of the work is required.

ADDITIVES IN CEMENT-BASED PLASTER MIXES

Plastering materials can also contain **additives** in liquid or powder form. These are either added during manufacture or during mixing.

Plasticiser is a liquid additive added to the mix to make it workable (easier to use). Without plasticiser, the mixed material will separate and become too heavy to spread. But too much plasticiser in the mix can make it weak, causing the mix to crumble.

Waterproofers and frostproofers are other types of additives. More information about these can be found in Chapters 4 and 6.

Silt

Fine grains of sand

Sand bulking

Sand containing water, making it swell and become heavy

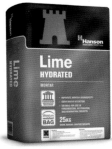

Hydrated lime

ACTIVITY

Research the differences between hydrated lime and hydraulic lime and how they set.

ACTIVITY

Research how cement and lime are manufactured.

Additive

A substance that we add to plaster mixes to change their natural properties

Plasticiser

PRE-MIXED PLASTER

Modern pre-mixed plasters are a mixture of gypsum and lightweight aggregates (vermiculite and perlite). There are a range of undercoat and setting coat plasters designed to be applied to different backgrounds. These plasters have many benefits:

- They will set hard in under two hours, allowing several applications within the same day.

- Their bonding capabilities are far greater than traditional plasters, which makes them more versatile.

- Setting coat plasters are made to provide an excellent surface finish that can be trowelled smooth for decoration. This type of plaster finish can be applied on sand and cement undercoats, plasterboard, and gypsum pre-mixed undercoat plaster.

You can learn more about plasters in Chapters 4, 6 and 7.

TOOLS AND EQUIPMENT

When mixing plaster, regardless of whether you are doing it by hand or using power tools, the first thing you need to do is set up your mixing area with the necessary tools. Use this table of tools as a checklist.

Tool	Use
Plunger/plasterer's mixing wheel	A traditional mixing tool used to mix the plaster when added to water. During and after the mixing process it should be kept off the floor to prevent any bits of debris from sticking to the bottom of the tool, which could contaminate the next mix.
Drill and whisk	A powerful motorised drill that mixes plaster with ease. It is a fast and efficient way of mixing lightweight plasters.

Tool	Use
Mixing stand 	This is an essential piece of equipment to keep the mixing tool off the ground, preventing it from picking up dirt and contaminating the mix. This will also prevent trailing leads which can cause trip hazards.
Bucket trowel and gauging trowel 	When mixing is in progress, either tool can be used to clean the rim of the mixing bucket, moving dry unmixed plaster back to the centre of the bucket.
Shovel 	This is used to scoop the plaster into the water. A paddle scoop can also be used.
Buckets or tubs 	Depending on the size of mix required, there are many types of mixing buckets. One bucket should be used for mixing and another for cleaning your mixing tools and equipment.
Hard hand brush 	This type of brush is used for cleaning tools and equipment. It has harder bristles than a standard brush and will not wear down as quickly.

CHOOSING YOUR MIXING AREA

The mixing area should have plenty of ventilation and clean air due to the amount of dust created from mixing plastering materials. Clean water and electricity are also required for mixing the plaster to the correct consistency.

The mixing area should be as close as possible to the stored material and have an area for disposing of waste materials. Mixing can be carried out inside or outside the work area.

Some designated mixing areas have protective floor coverings, such as plywood sheets, so that plaster spillages do not damage the floor surface. If you work in people's houses you can use dust sheets or cling film to protect the floor coverings and furniture.

A mixing area

Cement-based materials can be mixed in processing plants and delivered direct to site in a ready-mix lorry. When this method is chosen, the gauging process is known as 'batching' and is done by computer which is more accurate. This method is preferred when space is confined and there is no room for mixing.

A ready-mix lorry

MIXING PLASTERING MATERIALS

It is important to get the mixing right. Mixing plaster too wet can result in spillages and sagging. Mixing plaster too stiff can make it difficult to spread onto the background.

Sand and cement mixes are best mixed with a mechanical drum mixer. This will ensure that all materials are fully integrated and mixed together.

This type of mixing is carried out outdoors. It can be messy and noisy, and it's important to have a designated area where the mixer can be set up out of the way.

MIXING HAZARDS

There are many hazards associated with mixing. Learning about them will help you understand how to deal with them.

A mechanical drum mixer

ACTIVITY

With your tutor, carry out a maintenance check on the various types of mixers used in your college or workplace. Make a checklist.

Hazard	How to deal with it
Cement and lime can irritate and burn the skin	Wear gloves to protect your skin
Breathing in dust from bagged materials	Wear a dust mask to protect your lungs
Plaster splashes can get in the eyes	Wear protective glasses to protect your eyes
Mixing equipment creates a loud noise	Wear ear muffs or defenders to protect your ears
Trailing cables can cause trip hazards	Hang up cables so that they are out of the way, and wind them up and put them away after use
Badly maintained electrical equipment can cause an electric shock	Maintain the tools in a good state of repair, get them PAT tested, and carry out visual checks before use
Toxic fumes from petrol- or diesel-powered mixing equipment may cause dizziness and faintness	Use these pieces of equipment in well-ventilated areas or close to fume extraction units
Wet plaster on the floor can cause slips and falls	Cover the area with sand or saw dust to dry wet surfaces and highlight the hazard. Display warning signs or place barriers to cordon off the mixing area

Safety goggles

GAUGING MATERIALS

Gauging materials with buckets

'Gauging' is the term used for measuring materials. Gauging boxes were traditionally used to measure quantities of materials. Today, plastic buckets are preferred as they are lighter and have handles, which makes the job easier.

To measure quantities and volumes of materials accurately, fill the bucket or box to the top and then 'flatten off' with a piece of timber. This will ensure that the correct **proportion** of each material is added to make your mix.

It is extremely important to follow the **specification** when gauging plastering mixes and to gauge the materials accurately. Inaccurate mixing or gauging can lead to weakened mixes or mixes that are too strong.

You should avoid using damaged materials as they may have irregular setting times, **flash set** or have poor strength. Using materials and additives that have passed their use by date can affect the quality of strength causing poor surface finish. Damaged or out-of-date materials need to be placed to one side and reported to your supervisor.

MIXING TRADITIONAL CEMENT-BASED PLASTERING MATERIALS

You can mix traditional cement-based plastering materials, such as sand, cement and lime, either using machinery or by hand.

Proportion

The balance between different materials in a mix. When the balance is right, the materials are said to be 'in proportion'

Specification

A contract document that contains information on mix ratios and required standards of workmanship. This document will tell you how much of each material should be added to make the required mix

Flash set

When gypsum plasters have accelerated setting times, if mixed with dirty water or mixed using dirty equipment or tools

MIXING USING MACHINERY

The **ratio** for mixing sand, cement and lime in a drum mixer is 6:1:1 (although this can vary according to the specification). This is six parts sand, one part cement and one part lime. The process for this type of mixing is as follows.

1 Clean water and plasticiser should first be added to the mixer. This will prevent the other materials from sticking to the back of the drum.

2 Fill a bucket with sand, level the top and empty it into the mixer. Do this six times.

3 Gauge and add the cement and lime. One bucket of each will provide the correct ratio of 6:1:1.

4 When mixing is in process, the consistency of mixed material should be drier rather than wet. This will allow the plasticiser time to make the mix workable and make the plaster easier to use when applying.

5 Mixing should be carried out for at least five minutes, allowing the materials to fully mix together. Don't forget to wear goggles or glasses to protect your eyes from splashes from the turning drum of the mixer.

There are some instances where smaller amounts of mix are required. This can be mixed loose on a flat surface or in a bucket. Mixing by hand takes far longer and can be hard work, as we will see in the next section.

MIXING BY HAND

The following steps show how to mix cement-based plasters by hand.

Ratio

The proportion of materials that are mixed together, eg six parts sand to one part cement

INDUSTRY TIP

Be aware that the turning drum can cause serious injury.

STEP 1 First, gauge the materials.

STEP 2 Then, place the materials into a single pile.

STEP 3 Mix the materials dry (without adding water).

STEP 4 Once the materials are mixed, make a dip in the middle of the pile.

STEP 5 Measure the correct amount of plasticiser needed. To improve work-ability, add the plasticiser to the water.

STEP 6 Mix the plasticiser into the water.

STEP 7 Pour the water into the middle of the pile of material.

STEP 8 Using a shovel, pull the dry material slowly towards the centre, into the water.

INDUSTRY TIP

Don't add too much water or the mix will become too heavy, unworkable and difficult to use.

ACTIVITY

In groups of two or three, follow the procedure for mixing lime and sand mortar to a ratio of 3:1, plus plasticiser.

STEP 9 Mix and turn the material. The longer you turn, the better the mix.

STEP 10 The finished mix.

MIXING PRE-MIXED PLASTERS

Pre-mixed gypsum-based plasters can be mixed either by hand with a plunger or mechanically with a drill and whisk. When mixing, it is important to follow the manufacturer's technical instructions. These are normally printed on the back of the bag.

Irregular setting can occur when mixing this type of plaster if you do not follow the correct procedure of using clean water, tools and equipment.

The instructions will usually be similar to the following steps.

STEP 1 Quarter-fill a bucket or tub with clean water – this is for the mix. Three-quarters fill another bucket with clean water – this is for cleaning tools and equipment. Check the use by date of your plaster before use.

STEP 2 Add the plaster powder to the water and leave it to soak for several minutes; this will help start the mixing process. The longer you leave it, the easier it will be to mix.

STEP 3 Mix the plaster by rotating the plunger in a circular motion. It helps to also lift the plunger up and down. If the consistency is too wet, add some more powder and mix again until you get the correct consistency.

STEP 4 Clean the rim of the bucket with a bucket trowel, removing the dry plaster from the edge and back into the mix.

STEP 5 Continue to mix until the plaster has been fully mixed and there are no signs of any dry unmixed plaster (which will look lumpy).

ACTIVITY

Next time you're in the workshop or workplace, follow these steps for mixing a lightweight finishing plaster.

INDUSTRY TIP

If you're using a drill and whisk to mix the plaster, the procedure will be the same as using a plunger.

INDUSTRY TIP

Gypsum pre-mixed plasters set differently from cement-based plasters. They have less working time and will set hard within two hours. Gypsum plasters need to be used as soon as possible after the mixing process has begun.

Once the plaster has been mixed, the next stage is to clean the mixing tools and place them back in storage.

CALCULATING QUANTITIES

As a qualified plasterer, one of your roles will be to calculate the amount of materials and labour needed for given jobs or projects, so that you can **tender** for the work. Learning how to read measurements from scale drawings, working out costs and calculating labour can help you master this task. Spending time working out what materials you need for the job will ultimately be a cost-saving exercise, avoiding waste.

PERIMETER

Imagine you need to work out the perimeter of a room, for example to work out the quantity of EML strips needed to cover a wall plate perimeter and the number of fixings needed to attach them. This is calculated using **linear measurements**.

Example

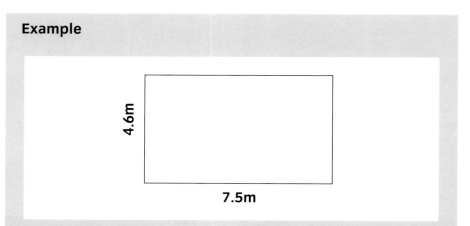

As explained in Chapter 2 (pages 59–61), the perimeter of the room can be measured by adding the length of all four walls. Using the above example, this would be:

$$4.6 + 7.5 + 4.6 + 7.5 = 24.2$$

The perimeter of the room is **24.2m**.

SURFACE AREA

When you apply plaster to a background wall, the wall is measured by area in square metres (m^2). Calculating the surface area for one whole wall in a room can be done using this simple formula:

length of the wall × height of the wall = area of the wall

Let's look at an example.

Example

A wall is 4.5m long by 2.4m high.

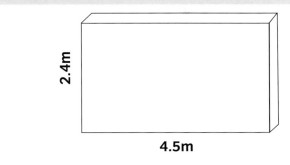

2.4m

4.5m

Using the formula, we simply multiply the length (4.5m) by the height (2.4m) to produce our area in m². Our calculations will look like this:

$$4.5 \times 2.4 = 10.8m^2$$

The amount of surface area to be plastered is **10.8m²**.

If there are any doors or windows in the wall, then the area of the doors and windows will need to be deducted from the total area. To do this, measure the openings and calculate their area using the same formula. Then subtract this from the total wall area. This will then give you the total area to be plastered in m². See Chapter 2, pages 62–64, for more information on calculating area.

PLASTER QUANTITIES

The table below will help you work out plaster quantities and indicate coverage for pre-mixed plaster. You can find this information in the manufacturer's information on the bags of plaster or in a plastering selector's guide.

Pre-mixed plaster per 25kg bag	Litres of water	Coverage	Thickness
Undercoat plaster	10.5l	4.5m²	9–10mm
Setting coat finish	11.5l	10.25m²	2–3mm

The table shows that one bag of setting coat finishing plaster applied 2–3mm thick will cover 10.25m². This means that in the area example, for a surface area of 10.8m², you will need two bags to cover this surface area, even though there will be plaster left over from the second bag.

INDUSTRY TIP

When you calculate the amount of plaster to be used, always allow for 10% wastage.

ACTIVITY

In pairs, measure a room and work out the surface area to be plastered. Calculate the amount of undercoat required to plaster the surface 9–10mm thick. Calculate the cost of labour and material required for the room. Remember to add 10% wastage to the total amount of plaster required.

A spray machine

ACTIVITY

Check out some websites of different plaster manufacturers and look at the types of plaster they produce.

Plasterers are often paid by the amount of plaster they apply onto the background surface. This is known as set price work. For example, for every square metre that the plasterer applies plaster to, he or she will receive £6.00 to cover material and labour costs.

Some plasters have been developed to be applied by machine. This is a fast, efficient way of applying plaster to a surface. Spray machines are quite powerful as they have to mix plaster and pump it through a hose before it sprays onto the surface. There are two methods for feeding plaster: this can be done by hand or the machine can be connected to a silo that contains the plaster. Silos contain dry pre-mixed plaster which can be delivered to site.

Case Study: Sara

Sara's neighbour asked her to over skim her living room wall with PVA and finishing plaster. She thought it was going to be a straightforward job.

When she got there, Sara noticed that the existing plaster had become loose and it had severe cracks in it. Sara explained that the plaster had become loose and it needed hacking back to the brickwork background. When this was done, the bricks in the background were smooth and had poor adhesion/key.

Sara explained that this type of surface would need a bonding slurry applied before re-plastering in order to improve adhesion between the plaster and background. It was important to follow the correct procedures when preparing the background in case it happened again.

Never assume a job will be easy until you've inspected it and confirmed all of the facts about the work.

Work through the following questions to check your learning.

1 Suction is tested on a background by
   a removing plaster
   b brushing the surface background
   c applying a sealer to the background
   d applying water to the surface.

2 High-suction backgrounds, such as aerated blocks, would benefit from
   a a solution of PVA mixed with water
   b dubbing out with plaster
   c raking the surface
   d an application of a bonding slurry.

3 Crazing/fire cracking in plasterwork can be a result of
   a the background having a poor key
   b a poorly mixed plaster
   c a high-suction background
   d no suction in the background.

4 Which one of the following tools will remove nails from a timber background?
   a Claw hammer.
   b Pointing trowel.
   c Scutch hammer.
   d Lump hammer.

5 Slurry coats are **best** used to bond
   a lime mortar
   b pre-mixed plaster
   c finishing plaster
   d cement mix.

6 The **best** tool for raking the joints of stonework is a
   a pointing hammer
   b lump hammer
   c crow bar
   d claw hammer.

7 Which one of the following is EML most likely to be fixed to?
   a Stone background.
   b Brick surfaces.
   c Timber wall plates.
   d Concrete lintels.

8 Backgrounds with hard, smooth surfaces require preparing with a
   a mechanical breaker and chisel attachment
   b scabbling tool
   c mechanical disc grinder
   d mechanical breaker and wire brush attachment.

9 Which one of the following is the correct sequence for mixing plaster?
   a Bucket, water, powder, mix and empty.
   b Water, powder, bucket, mix and empty.
   c Bucket, powder, water, mix and empty.
   d Bucket, mix, water, powder and empty.

10 For speed, pre-mixed plaster is **best** mixed with a
   a hand-held plunger
   b petrol drum mixer
   c electrical drum mixer
   d powered drill and whisk.

11 Flash set of plaster can be caused by mixing the plaster

   a   with clean water

   b   too wet

   c   dry

   d   with dirty water.

12 A consistent mix of cement-based plaster can be **best** achieved using a

   a   plunger

   b   drill and whisk

   c   mechanical drum mixer

   d   shovel and spot board.

13 Incorrect gauging of cement-based plaster will cause

   a   a good mix

   b   different strength of mix

   c   preferred set

   d   complete set.

14 Adding cement to a mix will

   a   increase its strength

   b   delay its set

   c   improve consistency

   d   make it cure quicker.

15 Which one of the following is a benefit of using lime in a cement-based plaster mix?

   a   Increase the strength of the mix.

   b   Improve the adhesion properties of the mix.

   c   Control suction.

   d   Make the mix heavy and dense.

16 Lightweight aggregate is found in

   a   pre-mixed plaster

   b   cement render

   c   lime

   d   sand.

17 Efflorescence is **most** likely to be found in a mix that contains

   a   crushed sand

   b   river sand

   c   sea sand

   d   crushed stone.

18 Pre-mixed plaster bags will **not** contain

   a   a use by date

   b   a production date

   c   mixing instructions

   d   mixing ingredients.

19 Plasticiser is added to cement-based mixes to improve the

   a   consistency

   b   strength

   c   colour

   d   workability.

20 When should plasticiser be added to the mix?

   a   At the start of the mixing process.

   b   After mixing.

   c   During the mixing process.

   d   Just before applying the plaster.

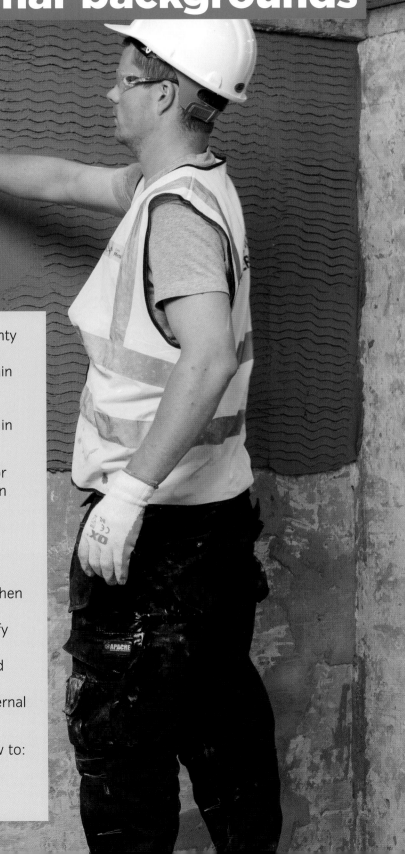

Chapter 4
Unit 122: Applying scratch coats to internal backgrounds

Plastering is an art that requires plenty of practice, patience and a lot of hands-on experience in order to gain the necessary skills to master the job. Learning how to apply a scratch coat will mean you have made significant progress in learning the plastering trade.

Scratch coats are most commonly used for straightening backgrounds that are uneven and can't be completed using a two coat system. They are the first coat of plaster applied to the background.

This chapter will help you develop the knowledge and understanding required when preparing to apply scratch coats to backgrounds. You will learn how to identify and select the relevant hand tools and equipment, and recognise and understand the need to select plasters that are compatible with the different types of internal background surfaces.

By reading this chapter you will know how to:

1 Apply scratch coats to internal backgrounds.

WHAT IS A SCRATCH COAT?

Scratch coats can be a mixture of traditional materials – that include loose sand, binders and additives – or a manufactured pre-mix. Whichever type is used, the scratch coat ingredients are mixed with clean water to make a suitable plaster material that is applied to internal background surfaces as the first coat of plaster. The background will then receive further coats in order to build up a flat surface on uneven backgrounds. This process, known as **three coat work**, includes the following applications:

1 *Scratch coat:* First application of plaster applied to the background.

2 *Floating coat:* Second application of plaster applied to the keyed scratch coat.

3 *Setting coat*: Third and final application of plaster applied to the floating coat.

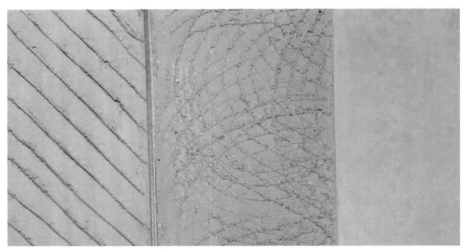

A typical example of three coat work may look like this. From left to right: scratch coat, floating coat and setting coat

Scratch coats are applied to uneven surfaces such as:

- stone
- slate
- old uneven brickwork
- concrete
- EML, called a 'pricking-up coat'.

Its purpose is to build up uneven surfaces in a layer of plaster – or, if the background is very uneven, more than one layer – preparing for the application of the floating coat.

Three coat work

The term used when a background requires several applications of plaster in order to straighten and cover uneven surfaces

Scratch coats are also applied to background surfaces that have been treated with a bonding adhesive for work that cannot be completed in two applications. For example, a brick background that has a straight flat surface but poor adhesion properties would need a slurry coat to improve adhesion. Therefore it would also require a scratch coat. This gives the plastered surface a good key and equal suction, allowing the next application of plaster to bond and grip with ease.

Severely uneven backgrounds may need more than one scratch coat to fill in the surface. A good example of this is the irregular shape of stone background surfaces, which often contain large and deep recessed joints. This type of background will need filling out first; the process for this is known as a 'dubbing out' coat. Applying excessive layers can cause the surface to sag and can result in poor bonding that can become loose from the background surface.

A completed scratch coat

A dubbing out coat applied to stone background joints

Before applying scratch coats, backgrounds should be checked to determine whether there are hollows or high points on the surface. This is best done using a straight edge (see page 139).

Once the scratch coat has been applied it will need to be keyed with a wire comb scratcher or scarifier. This leaves a horizontal groove pattern on the plaster surface, allowing later plaster coats to adhere to the scratch coat. The keying can be done in a straight line or wavy groove pattern.

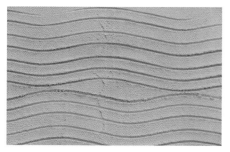

A wavy groove key with gaps would lead to poor key on the second application

A plastering trowel box

Keying a scratch coat with a wire comb scratcher to create an evenly keyed surface

Correctly applying the scratch coat to a background will provide a flat, straight surface with equal suction and a good key, allowing easy application of the floating coat.

TOOLS AND EQUIPMENT

All tradesmen require good quality equipment to carry out their work. The table below lists the basic tools and equipment that you will need in order to apply a scratch coat.

Tool	Use
Hawk 	Used to hold and transfer a workable amount of plaster from the spot board to the wall. The hawk is used in conjunction with the trowel to manipulate and apply the plaster directly onto the background surface. Some plasterers prefer hawks with detachable handles as they are easier to store. They were traditionally made from timber, but modern hawks are made from polyurethane or aluminium.
Comb scratcher 	Used to form a key on scratch coats. A comb scratcher is generally used on cement-based plasters.

Tool	Use
Scarifier	Like a comb scratcher, this is used to form a key on scratch coats. A scarifier is preferred on lightweight plaster surfaces.
Straight/feather edge	Made from aluminium, this tool has many uses. Its main use will be to rule plaster surfaces and check for straightness. Another use is to form angles or the edges of returns and reveals before fitting them with standard angle beads. (This will be explained later in Chapter 6.) Note: a feather edge is a type of straight edge.
Darby	This tool has many uses. One is to rule and flatten scratch coat surfaces. Another is to form the angles of returns and reveals on uneven surfaces.
Large bristled brush	A large bristled brush has many uses, such as cleaning tools and equipment, or applying water or slurries to backgrounds.
Floor scraper	A floor scraper is often used with a sweeping brush for cleaning the work area during and after applying the scratch coat. Wet plastering materials can cause a slippery surface and need to be cleared up as soon as possible to prevent slips.
Sweeping brush	*See* 'Floor scraper'.

INDUSTRY TIP

Make sure you keep your equipment clean. Plaster left on the tool's surface can be difficult to clean off once it has gone hard.

Tool	Use
Plasterer's trowel 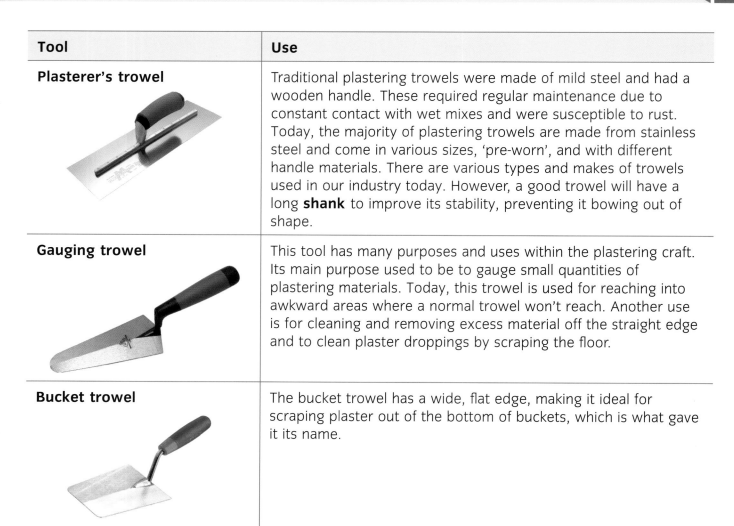	Traditional plastering trowels were made of mild steel and had a wooden handle. These required regular maintenance due to constant contact with wet mixes and were susceptible to rust. Today, the majority of plastering trowels are made from stainless steel and come in various sizes, 'pre-worn', and with different handle materials. There are various types and makes of trowels used in our industry today. However, a good trowel will have a long **shank** to improve its stability, preventing it bowing out of shape.
Gauging trowel	This tool has many purposes and uses within the plastering craft. Its main purpose used to be to gauge small quantities of plastering materials. Today, this trowel is used for reaching into awkward areas where a normal trowel won't reach. Another use is for cleaning and removing excess material off the straight edge and to clean plaster droppings by scraping the floor.
Bucket trowel	The bucket trowel has a wide, flat edge, making it ideal for scraping plaster out of the bottom of buckets, which is what gave it its name.

Shank

The part of a trowel that spreads out from the handle along the back of the flat face, attaching them together

As well as your tools, you will need equipment to apply scratch coats. The table below shows the equipment you will need and explains their use.

Equipment	Use
Spot board and stand	These are used to hold the plaster mix. They should be set out on a flat area as close as possible to the wall in order to reduce the need to transfer the material over long distances, which can be heavy and tiring work. A good spot board should be made from 18mm thick plywood that will not warp or bend. It should also be clean when plaster is placed onto its surface. The spot board stand is made from steel and will normally have four legs to take the weight of the spot board at each corner when loaded with the mix. Spot board stands are designed to be erected and dismantled with ease, so they take up less space when not in use.

Equipment	Use
Wheelbarrow 	Transporting plastering material over distances can be hard and heavy work. Using a wheelbarrow can make the job easier and less strenuous.
Shovel 	Used to lift and transport materials.
Hop-up or platform with staging 	Purpose-made access equipment made of aluminium or timber that allows you to work up to standard ceiling heights. Its design allows you to step onto a platform from the ground without stretching.
Buckets 	Buckets and tubs have many uses for plastering, including transporting materials and clean water, and for mixing.
Tool bag 	A plasterer's tool kit contains many items that will need to be maintained and cleaned after use. The tool bag or holdall can be used to store them safely and securely, helping to keep them damage free and prolonging their life.

INDUSTRY TIP

A good way of plastering the top of a wall is to set up two hop-ups, one at each end of the wall, with two scaffold boards rested between them. This will make a good staging, allowing you to complete your work methodically and safely along the top edge of the wall.

INDUSTRY TIP

There is a saying: 'Buy cheap, buy twice.' This means that, if you buy cheap tools, you are likely to have to replace them more often than if you had bought better-quality equivalents.

Compatible

In a plastering context, this is when the plaster materials used are the right strength for the background they are applied to

Symbols

Used on drawings to indicate different types of building materials

Ratio

The proportion of materials that are mixed together, eg six parts sand to one part cement

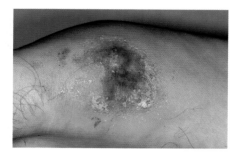

Skin burns from cement

MATERIALS USED FOR SCRATCH COATS

When preparing to apply a scratch coat to a wall, you need to familiarise yourself with the type of plastering materials that you are about to apply to the surface. You can use drawings, specifications and other contract documents as sources of information about the work. The drawing and specification will tell you what type of materials should be used and also provide information on the backgrounds, allowing you to prepare your work.

The architect is responsible for producing working drawings and during the design stage they will decide on the specific materials to be used for the plastering work. The plaster materials chosen for the scratch coat should be **compatible** with the background and will be listed in the specification.

The drawings will include **symbols** to show the walls/backgrounds that need scratch coats. They will also show relevant room layouts and access to them, plus the measurements and therefore the size of the surfaces to be plastered. Refer back to Chapter 2 for more information on standard symbols and drawings.

The specification will provide information on **ratios**, the type of scratch coat mixes, the application method, and the desired thickness, workmanship and standards. All this information is vital and will help you plan precise work methods. Poor planning will increase your workload and cost more money.

Refer back to Chapter 3, pages 118–122, for more information on the materials used in scratch coats.

Different types of plastering materials and additives are used for mixing scratch coats, some of which contain harmful substances. It is always important to understand the health and safety requirements for different plastering materials. Make it a habit to read the manufacturer's data sheet on the safe use of their materials – this can help protect you and your work colleagues from injuries such as irritation and skin burns.

TYPES OF BACKGROUND SURFACES FOR SCRATCH COATS

STONE, SLATE AND OLD BRICKWORK BACKGROUNDS

Stone, slate and old brickwork are best plastered with traditional mixes that include sand, cement and lime, plus a plasticiser. Scratch coats can be applied on this type of background surface to a thickness of approximately 9–11mm. Cement-based scratch coats are best left to cure and shrink over several days before the next coat is applied.

HIGH-SUCTION BACKGROUNDS

Applying scratch coats over high-suction backgrounds should be avoided: loss of moisture from the applied mix can cause crazing cracks to appear on the surface, making the plaster become weak and powdery. This can be avoided by treating the suction with water. If the suction rate persists and can't be controlled with water then a solution of one part water and five parts PVA can be applied to seal the surface.

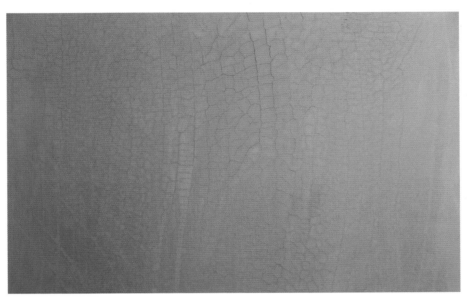

Crazing cracks

CONCRETE LINTELS AND PAD STONES

Scratch coats can also be applied to concrete lintels and pad stones. However, if you are using traditional cement-based plaster then these will need to be prepared beforehand with a bonding slurry.

PRE-CAST CONCRETE SURFACES

Pre-cast concrete surfaces are best plastered using a lightweight **pre-mixed plaster** which has high adhesion due to its irregular shape that increases its stickiness.

Thistle Bonding is a lightweight pre-mixed plaster manufactured by British Gypsum. It is designed to be applied on low-suction backgrounds, such as concrete or plasterboard, or on backgrounds with poor adhesion properties, such as expanded metal lath (EML). The recommended thickness of application is a minimum of 8mm. However, due to its lightness compared with cement-based plasters, it can be applied much thicker. Lightweight plasters are keyed using a scarifier or comb scratcher when applied as a scratch coat.

Pre-mixed plaster

Plaster materials that have been mixed in a processing plant and are sold bagged, only needing clean water added for mixing

Pre-mixed bonding coat plaster

WALLS WITH DAMP PROBLEMS

Limelight plasters are pre-mixed cement- and lime-based plasters that include a lightweight aggregate known as **perlite**. This type of plaster is mainly used for walls that have damp problems and have been treated with a chemical damp course. The process of application is the same as applying sand and cement plasters, and will need to be left for several days to dry between subsequent coats.

Perlite

A lightweight aggregate used in pre-mixed plastering materials for scratch coats

Lime-based pre-mixed plaster

EXPANDED METAL LATHING (EML)

Expanded metal lathing (EML) requires a backing coat, known as a 'pricking-up coat', before it is floated and finished with a setting coat. The pricking-up coat is applied and trowelled into the EML's diamond-patterned mesh surface which provides reinforcement for the plaster base. When completed, the pricking-up coat should be keyed diagonally to prevent the plaster from sagging. EML can be plastered using traditional sand and cement-based plaster or lightweight bonding-grade plaster.

INDUSTRY TIP

Catch boards are sometimes placed directly beneath the wall being plastered to catch any droppings that come from the surface when applying the scratch coat. This protects the floor. This is a good way of keeping the work area clean, preventing any slip hazards.

Applying plaster over EML

OUR HOUSE

Once you have prepared the wall plates in 'Our House', the next stage is to prepare that surface with a scratch coat before applying the floating coat. This coat is called a pricking-up coat.

1   Select a suitable undercoat plaster that will be compatible with this surface. Give your reasons for using this type of plaster.
2   Provide the manufacturer's instructions on this type of plaster.
3   Provide a list of the tools and equipment that you will need to carry out the plastering work.
4   What are the health and safety issues to be considered?

CALCULATING MATERIALS

Calculating which materials you require and how much of it is an essential part of a plasterer's job. Ordering too much material can be costly and your profit will be lost. Ordering too little can affect the progress of the work and cost you money in standing labour.

When **pricing for work** you will have to work out how much of each material you need for the specified area to be plastered. You can do this by measuring and calculating the wall area from the drawings. Once you have the measurements and calculations, the next stage is to find out the ratio of the mix – this will allow you to work out the amount of each material that you need – and how thick the scratch coat is to be applied. Reading the specification will help you do this.

Pricing for work

Calculating and costing for plastering work

ACTIVITY

A 45m² area of walling requires plastering 10mm thick. Using the data in the example, calculate how many 25kg bags of sand and cement are required. Don't forget to allow for wastage

Answer: 3 bags of cement and a bag of sand

Example

You are using the ratio 4 of sand to 1 of cement applied 10mm thick to a wall.

- One 25kg bag of cement will cover 4.5m² at 10mm thick.
- One 25kg bag of sand will also cover 4.5m² at 10mm thick.

If the mix required is 4 sand to 1 cement (4:1 mix), it will cover 22.5m² of wall. The calculation for this is the total number of bags multiplied by the area each bag covers:

$5 \times 4.5 = 22.5m^2$

If you have a wall area that measures 225m², how many 25kg bags of sand and cement applied 10mm thick will you need if you use the ratio 4 sand to 1 cement? Use the data above for your calculations.

The answer is as follows:

Divide your wall area by the area that the 4:1 mix covers.

$225 \div 22.5 = 10$ (bags)

So you will need $4 \times 10 = 40$ bags of sand and $1 \times 10 = 10$ bags of cement to complete the job.

To allow for minor errors, we should always add extra for wastage, normally 10%. You need to work this out for the sand *and* cement.

- Sand: 10% of 40 is 4.
- Cement: 10% of 10 is 1.

So you would need another 4 bags of sand and 1 bag of cement. This brings the total for the job of **44** bags of sand and **11** bags of cement.

SCRATCH COAT MIXES

MIX RATIOS

Cement-based ratios for dubbing out and scratch coats can vary depending on the characteristics of the background. In some cases, the background may have penetrating or rising damp, which is quite common in old housing. This will mean that the ratio of the mix will be different compared with walls that have no damp issues but may have poor adhesion and key.

The following table shows the ratio of mixes for scratch coats and dubbing out.

Ratio of mixes	Use
Ratio (written as 6:1:1) of: 6 sand 1 cement 1 lime plus plasticiser. **Ratio (7:1:1) of:** 7 sand 1 cement 1 lime plus plasticiser.	These ratios of mix would be preferred on severe uneven backgrounds, such as stone or old brickwork. In some cases, less lime is added; however, this will depend on the specification.
Ratio (3:1) of: 3 sand 1 cement plus waterproofer. **Ratio (4:1) of:** 4 sand 1 cement plus waterproofer.	These ratios of mix would be preferred when dubbing out and applying scratch coats to backgrounds that have been treated for rising or penetrating damp.
Ratio (4:1) of: 4 sand 1 cement.	This ratio is preferred when applying scratch coats on to slurry surfaces.
Ratio (5:1) of: 5 sand 1 cement.	This mix would be used on uneven surfaces that have good key, and only requires preparing with water or PVA.
Ratio (5:2) of: 5 sand 2 lime.	Used for training purposes in colleges.

Mixing cement-based plaster

Mixes can vary depending on the background and area to be covered. Always follow the specification when mixing materials.

PREVENTING FAULTS IN SCRATCH COAT MIXES

When you are mixing cement, lime and sand for a scratch coat, you should always gauge your materials accurately and add the correct amount of additive. If for any reason the plastered surface fails and becomes problematic, faults in plastered surfaces can be tested and diagnosed in laboratories.

INDUSTRY TIP

Strong mix ratios – such as 3:1 sand and cement – are deemed too hard and brittle, and can shrink and crack.

Some uneven backgrounds will benefit from having lime in the mix due to its adhesive properties. Lime also provides suction, drawing moisture from the next coat and helping it to set. Lime also reduces shrinkage, which prevents cracking.

Waterproofer is a good additive that is used in scratch coat mixes on surfaces that have been treated for rising or penetrating damp. Waterproofer is a liquid formula added to the water when mixing. It prevents moisture from passing or penetrating through the plaster and coming through to the surface.

Waterproofer in different containers

Always follow the manufacturer's instructions when measuring out and adding additives to scratch coat mixes. If you add too much or too little, the mix can lose its strength and become weak. Its intended use within the mix will also be affected, which could lead to moisture passing through the scratch coat surface.

After applying your scratch coat, it should be left to cure for several days before applying the next coat. This allows any shrinkage to take place. It is recommended that the subsequent or following coats be the same strength or slightly weaker. Applying stronger material onto weaker backgrounds or backing coats can cause stress, resulting in the scratch coat cracking or blowing from the surface.

TEST MIXING

To test different scratch coat mixes, follow the steps below.

ACTIVITY

Carry out a test, mixing small amounts of scratch coat material in small jars using the following ratios and additive:

Test 1: mix ratio 6:1:1 with plasticiser.
Test 2: mix ratio 4:1 with waterproofer.

Sand   Cement

STEP 1 Mix two different scratch coat mixes – one with plasticiser and one with waterproofer. Leave to dry for several days until all the moisture has evaporated from the mixed plaster.

Plasticiser   Waterproofer

STEP 2 Place the scratch coat mixes in different containers.

Plasticiser   Waterproofer

STEP 3 Leave to dry for several days until all the moisture has evaporated from the mixed plaster.

STEP 4 Add the same amount of water to two containers. Place a mark on the containers to indicate the water level.

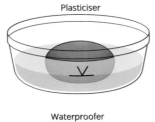

Plasticiser

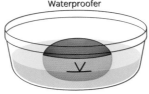

Waterproofer

STEP 5 Place the scratch coat samples in the containers and leave for one minute.

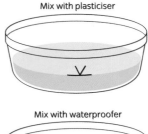

Mix with plasticiser

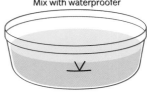

Mix with waterproofer

STEP 6 Check to see which scratch coat sample mix has absorbed the least and most amount of water.

STORAGE AREAS

You need to set aside an area for storing the bagged materials such as sand, cement, pre-mixed plasters and additives. If the materials are being delivered to the site, you should make sure that this area has good access, too.

Loose sand can be stored outside, preferably on a flat surface covered by a strong tarpaulin to protect it from wind, rain and **contamination**. Bagged materials need to be stored inside on pallets, off the ground

Contamination

When materials have been negatively affected, eg by leaves blown into the sand or by using dirty water for mixing

Bagged materials stacked in a storage area

Shelf life
The use by date of the product or material

and away from moisture. Liquid additives also need to be stored stacked inside so that they are protected from frost.

A good storage area will allow for stock control, so that materials and additives are used within their **shelf life**.

MIXING AREAS

Your mixing area will depend on the type of mix you are using.

- Cement-based mixes are best mixed outside in a drum mixer. This can be noisy and the materials used will cause high dust levels.

- Pre-mixed plasters are generally mixed inside the building, using a powerful drill and whisk. A designated mixing area will be required, with access to electricity and water.

An outdoor mixing area

An indoor mixing area

INDUSTRY TIP
Always put new deliveries at the back of the stock pile, ensuring that the older materials are used first. This is known as 'stock rotation'.

APPLYING SCRATCH COATS

HEALTH AND SAFETY ISSUES

Before you apply scratch coats, you need to be aware of the risks involved, both in general and in the specific place where you are working. Read the risk assessment to help you identify these and make you aware of the dangers involved with the plastering work. Wearing appropriate safety clothing and using equipment correctly will also help reduce the risk of injury. As you will see in the steps on pages 152–153, you need to wear a hi-viz jacket, gloves, glasses, boots and a helmet.

Wearing appropriate clothing for applying scratch coats

PREPARATION

The key to a successful job is preparing the work area and equipment beforehand. This will make completing the job as straightforward as possible. Listening to your tutor or supervisor will help you plan your work area, improving the efficiency of your work and reducing any risk of accidents.

The first thing you need to do is load the spot board with the mix, using a shovel and wheelbarrow, as shown in the steps below.

STEP 1 Load the wheelbarrow with sand–lime mix and transport it to your spot board.

STEP 2 Use the shovel to lift the mixed material from the rear of the wheel-barrow.

STEP 3 Load the spot board with the mix.

Applying a scratch coat onto a background is a tricky skill to learn. Before you can carry out this process properly you will need to learn other hands-on skills and techniques, such as transferring mixed plaster from the spot board to the wall using the hawk and plastering trowel. Learning how to use the hawk and trowel and becoming confident with this technique will make the job of plastering much easier for you to master.

ACTIVITY

Ask your tutor to show you the process for using a hawk and trowel.

STEP 1 Dampen the hawk with water.

STEP 2 Retrieve the plastering material onto the hawk.

STEP 3 Lift the hawk and remove it from the spot board.

STEP 4 Turn the plaster material with the plastering trowel.

STEP 5 Remove the plaster from the hawk, ready for applying to the background.

APPLICATION

You are now ready to begin applying the scratch coat. The step-by-step guide below shows how to apply a scratch coat to a plain wall with a brick background, using the techniques we just covered.

STEP 1 Mix the different materials and include the plasticiser, which will give the mix its workability.

STEP 2 Load the spot board. Next, set up your hop-up. This will give you a platform that allows you to reach the ceiling height of the wall.

STEP 3 Wet the background surface using a brush to reduce the suction.

STEP 4 Transfer the plastering material from the spot to the wall using your hawk and trowel.

STEP 5 Apply the scratch coat, starting at the top-right corner (if you are right-handed) or the top-left corner (if you are left-handed), laying four trowel widths apart and in lengths of 300mm long. The plaster should then be flattened using the trowel at a shallow angle to help spread the material. The applied scratch coat needs to be about 10mm thick.

STEP 6 Working downwards and across, follow the same procedure until you have applied an area of 1m². It is best to break the wall surface into sections as this is more efficient and will help you complete the work in a methodical order.

STEP 7 This section of the surface is now ready to be keyed using a comb scratcher. The surface should be keyed horizontally, deep enough to allow the next coat to grip but not so deep as to penetrate through the scratch coat to the background.

STEP 8 Apply the scratch coat to the rest of the wall and key it, using the same procedure.

STEP 9 Once the wall has been plastered, check its surface with a straight edge. Fill in any hollows or remove excessive thickness, preparing the surface to receive the next layer once the scratch coat has set.

STEP 10 Once the wall is complete, the next stage is to clean the work area: wet or messy surfaces are a slip hazard.

ACTIVITY

Ask your tutor to fix two lengths of 10mm thick timber onto a wall to act as guides. Apply a scratch coat onto the surface between the timbers, using a straight edge to check how flat and thick you have laid your plaster. You can also rule the surface with a straight edge, using the timber as guides. Once the surface is flat and straight, key the surface with a comb scratcher.

FORMING EXTERNAL ANGLES TO UNEVEN BRICKWORK

Return

Where a wall turns a corner, forming a right angle

INDUSTRY TIP

Always prime your straight edge with water before use; this will prevent the plaster from sticking to its surface.

The skills required to apply scratch coats to a simple wall can take several weeks to master. When you have, you are ready to move on to the next stage, which involves plastering walls that include **returns** and reveals. It is slightly more difficult to learn this technique and you will need help from a work colleague to carry out this task successfully. This will be covered in greater depth at Level 2.

The following steps show you how to apply a scratch coat to a return.

STEP 1 Hold a straight edge or feather edge on its face to one side of the return and check it is being held plumb. The edge of the straight edge should be set forward from the face, allowing for the thickness of scratch coat to cover the background surface. The thickness should be about 10mm.

STEP 2 Apply the scratch coat up to the straight edge.

STEP 3 Once you have applied the scratch coat, carefully remove the straight edge by tilting its face and gently sliding it away from the **arris**, leaving a sharp corner.

STEP 4 Clean the straight edge.

STEP 5 Repeat the process on the other side of the angle.

STEP 6 Key the surface with a comb scratcher horizontally, working away from the arris.

Arris

Where two walls meet to form an angle

When you need to form a return on uneven surfaces such as stone or slate, the process is slightly different from the above.

Instead of using an aluminium straight edge, a planed timber rule should be used.

1 Before you start, check that the timber is straight and not warped. Wet its face to prevent any suction from the timber.

2 Position the timber, then lean **struts** against it to hold it in place. The timber must be held in place firmly.

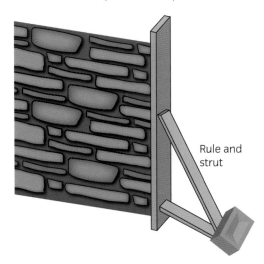

Rule and strut

Forming a return using a timber rule

3 Apply the plaster to the return, working up to the timber rule, and key the surface.

4 Due to the likely excessive thickness of the coat because of the uneven surface, the rule is left in position overnight to allow the scratch coat to set.

5 The following day, carefully remove the struts and timber rule, cleaning any plaster from the timber's face.

6 Next, position the timber and struts on the other side of the return and repeat the process.

This should leave a clean sharp corner allowing you to fix your angle beads. (Angle beads are covered in Chapter 5.)

ACTIVITY

When you are next in the workshop or workplace, try this procedure for forming a return: ask someone else to hold the straight edge for you and take turns to form one side of the return. Before you start, make a list of the tools that you will need in order to carry out the work and set up for the task.

Strut

Timber used to position the timber rule, to prevent it from moving whilst plastering up to the corner

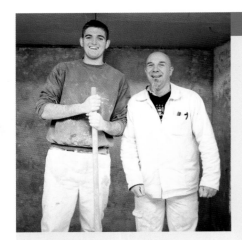

Case Study: Wayne and Henry

Wayne's first ever plastering job was on a stone background, which meant he first had to dub it out. The background was severely uneven and Wayne's supervisor, Henry, explained that Wayne would have to give it several coats of sand and cement scratch coat materials in order to build it out.

The mix ratio was stipulated on the specification: the dubbing out scratch coat ratio was 4 sand:1 cement with a waterproofed additive. Wayne made sure he read the manufacturer's instructions on the back of the container before measuring the additive and adding it to the water. He then measured the sand and cement material in buckets and added them to the mixer to make the mix – he had heard that this is the best way to make sure the mix is consistent in strength. Wayne made the mix quite stiff in order to build out in between the stone joints, which were deep and needed to be treated for suction by gently splashing with water.

After completing the wall, Wayne keyed it with a comb scratcher and left it to dry for two days, allowing it to cure and shrink.

The next scratch coat was a ratio of 6 sand:1 cement:1 lime, which is slightly weaker than the dubbing out coat – lime is good for adhesion and provides suction for the next layer. This time the additive was plasticiser which made the next coat easy to spread. Wayne applied the scratch coat to the wall and checked it for straightness using a straight edge, before keying the surface with a comb scratcher, ready for the floating coat. Henry checked the wall and was pleased with the work Wayne had done.

Work through the following questions to check your learning.

1   Which one of the following coat work applications is a scratch coat part of?

a   One.

b   Two.

c   Three.

d   Four.

2   Dubbing out coats are applied to

a   uneven backgrounds

b   flat backgrounds

c   straight surfaces

d   skimmed surfaces.

3   Waterproofer is added to the mix to prevent

a   quick curing

b   fast drying

c   penetrating damp

d   increased set.

4   Scratch coats can be keyed using a

a   comb scratcher

b   gauging trowel

c   bucket trowel

d   mixing tool.

5   Lime is added to cement-based scratch coats to improve

a   consistency and colour

b   strength and weakness

c   adhesion and suction

d   curing and shrinkage.

6   Which one of the following is contained in mixed scratch coats for strength?

a   Cement.

b   Waterproofer.

c   Plasticiser.

d   Lime.

7   Manufacturers' instructions will provide information on

a   binders

b   aggregates

c   setting times

d   plaster strength.

8   Which one of the following types of PPE should be worn when applying scratch coats?

a   Dust mask.

b   Ear muffs.

c   Glasses.

d   Laps.

9   Mix ratios can be found in the

a   schedule

b   drawing

c   specification

d   bill of quantities.

10   When measuring quantities of materials, measurements are taken from the

a   drawing

b   schedule

c   risk assessment

d   method statement.

11   Which one of the following tools is used for checking walls before applying the floating coat?

a   Hawk.

b   Trowel.

c   Straight edge.

d   Comb scratcher.

12 Another term for dubbing out is

a   scratch coat

b   base coat

c   application

d   penetration.

13 Which one of the following applications follows a scratch coat?

a   Set and scratch.

b   Set and float.

c   Float and set.

d   Finish and set.

14 If the scratch coats sags after application, this is the result of it being applied

a   too thinly

b   to the base of the wall

c   from the top of the wall

d   too thickly.

15 EML is keyed

a   horizontally

b   vertically

c   diagonally

d   across.

16 Scratch coats are keyed to

a   prevent suction

b   allow the next coat to bond

c   prevent moisture

d   improve workability.

17 How thickly is a scratch coat applied?

a   4mm.

b   6mm.

c   8mm.

d   10mm.

18 Cement-based scratch coats are **best** mixed using a

a   drill and whisk

b   mechanical drum mixer

c   plunger

d   bucket trowel.

19 When gauging scratch coat material, for consistency and strength it is **best** done with a

a   trowel

b   bucket

c   shovel

d   scoop.

20 Scratch coats applied to the background **should** be

a   bulky

b   fatty

c   stronger

d   compatible.

Chapter 5
Unit 123: Fixing sheet materials

This unit is about measuring, cutting and fixing sheet materials, specifically expanded metal lathing (EML), pre-formed beads and plasterboards. These materials are widely used in modern construction because of their speed of installation, ease of use and ability to be used for different applications. Sheet materials offer the builder a high-performance finish with dramatically reduced costs when compared with many of the more traditional plastering methods.

Modern plasterers will be using sheet materials on an almost daily basis and need to know about the different types of sheet materials, their uses and their limitations.

By reading this chapter you will know how to:

1 Measure, cut and fix plasterboard.
2 Measure, cut and fix pre-formed beads and EML.

MEASURING, CUTTING AND FIXING PLASTERBOARD

Wooden lath

Thin strips of wood 1.5m long, 30mm wide and 6mm thick that were traditionally fixed to studwork and ceilings. They were used before the widespread use of plasterboards and EML to form a background for plasterwork

Stud walling/studwork

A partition wall constructed from lengths of timber that make a frame to fix sheet materials to

Before the invention of plasterboard, plasterers had to fix **wooden laths** to timber-framed backgrounds such as ceilings and **stud walling/studwork**. These laths formed a suitable background that would then receive three coats of plaster. It was a time-consuming and labour-intensive process.

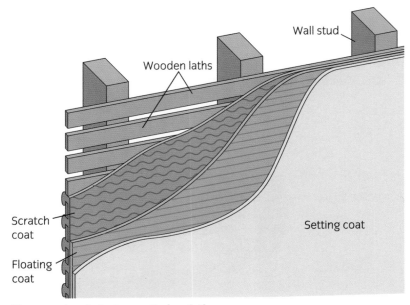

Three coats of plaster on timber laths

A wooden lath ceiling

Drying time

The time that needs to pass between applying a plaster coat or coats and being able to decorate

With the introduction of plasterboard, the process of installing ceilings and stud walls was speeded up dramatically, reducing labour costs and **drying time** as the boards need only receive a finish coat of plaster. This meant that buildings became quicker to finish.

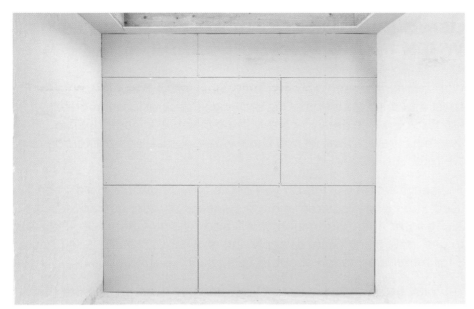

Plasterboard installed on a stud wall

Skimming plasterboard

An alternative to applying a finish coat of plaster to plasterboard is a process called 'tape and joining'. We will touch on this process a little later in this chapter. However, it will be covered in more detail at Level 2.

Tape and joining

USING SPECIFICATIONS AND SCHEDULES WHEN FIXING PLASTERBOARDS

When working on site, you may be given a set of drawings and a specification to work from. One drawing (a general location drawing) will tell you which area you are working in, while another one (an assembly drawing) will let you know where in that area plasterboards are to be installed.

The specification will inform you of the type of plasterboard to be used, the fixings required and the standard of work demanded. Along with other information, it will also tell you what type of plaster to use, how many coats to apply and at what thickness. (See Chapter 2 for more information about drawings and specifications.)

You may be given these instructions verbally. If so, make sure that you understand them. Write the instructions down if necessary and then repeat them back to the person who is giving them to you. If possible, have them sent by email or text, so that you have a record of what you are being asked to do. This will minimise the chance of a mistake occurring. If a mistake does occur, as long as you did exactly what was asked of you then you cannot be held responsible.

MEASURING ACCURATELY

When taking any measurement, it is important to be as accurate as possible. What may be a simple mistake such as reading the wrong number off a tape measure or putting the decimal point in the wrong place can in fact prove very costly. If it goes unnoticed for any length of time, it can cause delay to the job whilst the error is put right, costing money.

Measuring plasterboard wrongly does not just cost the price of the plasterboard: it also costs the time to do it again and the cost of disposing of the plasterboard that you have to throw away. If you are paying for the materials, this is a mistake that you will not want to make too often. If somebody else is paying for materials, they will be asking questions when the plasterboards run out and the skips are full. When working on a **price**, your supervisor may ask you to measure up the amount of work you have completed at the end of the week. If you misread the tape measure, you may not get paid for all the work you have done.

TYPES OF PLASTERBOARD

Plasterboard has come a long way since its invention near the start of the 20th century. Modern plasterboards, such as standard performance wall board, provide a suitable background for plastering, tiling or decorating. There is also a wide range of specialised boards specifically designed to perform well under a variety of different conditions. These include:

- fire-resistant boards
- soundproofing boards
- moisture-resistant boards
- impact-resistant boards
- vapour barriers
- insulating boards.

Some of the higher specification boards will perform more than one of those functions – or even all of them! Each manufacturer publishes a datasheet giving the **specifications** and **limitations** of its product. The different types of plasterboard are also colour coded for ease of identification.

Moisture-resistant boards are green, fire-resistant is pink, soundproofed is blue and insulating board (also known as thermal board) and impact board tend to be the normal cream/ivory colour. You will learn more about this at Level 2.

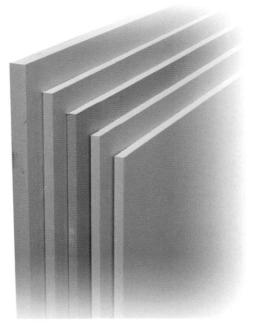

Plasterboard in different colours

ACTIVITY

Go online and investigate the types of plasterboard available from different plasterboard suppliers, such as British Gypsum, Knauf and Lafarge.

Specification

Manufacturers' specifications say what a product may be used for, how it is to be installed and what conditions it can be exposed to. Not to be confused with a job specification that tells you how a specific job should be carried out

Limitations

The extent to which a material can be safely employed, for example how long the material can withstand fire. Beyond this, it becomes unsafe or ineffective

ACTIVITY

Compare the thicknesses of different plasterboards.

Building regulations state that a building must conform to certain standards, including:

- *minimum fire check times*: the least amount of time allowed before a fire burns through a building's structure such as walls, doors and ceilings

- *maximum heat loss*: the maximum amount of heat that can be lost through a building's structure such as windows, walls, ceilings and roofs

- *maximum noise levels*: the volume of noise allowed to be heard from neighbouring properties, through partition walls floors and ceilings etc.

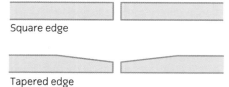

Square edge

Tapered edge

Plasterboards with square and tapered edges

Square edge

Square-edge plasterboards have their edges cut at a 90° angle from their face

Tapered edge

Tapered-edge plasterboards are cut at a slant

When designing buildings, architects have to work within these regulations. They also have to work to their clients' requirements, as long as they conform to building regulations. These factors help determine which plasterboard is used and where.

Another factor that helps determine the type of plasterboard is the distance between the studs or joists – the greater the distance between the studs or joists, the thicker and therefore more rigid the plasterboard must be.

All of the above types of plasterboards come in a variety of lengths, widths and thicknesses. They also have either a **square edge** or a **tapered edge**.

The most common sizes of plasterboards, including the correct fixing sizes, can be found in the table below.

Thickness of board in mm	Minimum size of screw in mm
9.5	32
12.5	38
15	38
19	42

Although these boards have different properties and specifications, the thing they have in common is how they are made. They are made from basically pure gypsum, a by-product of some power stations, mixed into a slurry with recycled plasterboards from building sites and plasterboard manufacturers. Once additives have been added, which give the finished boards their particular characteristics, the slurry is poured onto a continuous sheet of specially designed lining paper.

The lining paper is then lapped up the sides and over the top of the slurry to form the **bound edge**. Another sheet of lining paper holds the bottom sheet in place, sandwiching the slurry between the two sheets of lining paper. The continuous sheet then passes through a series of rollers to obtain the correct thickness, then into a kiln to dry out before being cut to the required length, forming the **unbound edge**.

Plasterboard being manufactured

Bound edge

The long edge of the plasterboard where the lining paper is wrapped up around the sides

Unbound edge

The short edge of a plasterboard sheet where the core is visible

Laminate boards

Some boards have insulation stuck to the back of them. These are known as laminate boards and are used where extra insulation is required.

STORING AND HANDLING PLASTERBOARDS

Plasterboards are fragile and easily damaged. They will bow if stored upright, and if kept in damp conditions they will soak up moisture and **deteriorate**. Correct storage and handling are essential to help prevent damage from occurring. Plasterboards should be:

- stored flat

- kept under cover, in dry conditions

- kept off the ground and well supported

- stacked no more than 1m high.

Deteriorate

To become worse in quality and strength

Always observe the correct manual handling techniques and health and safety requirements when handling or moving plasterboards. A risk assessment and safe system of work will tell you of the possible dangers when handling plasterboards, the safest way of working and the correct PPE to be used.

Because of their awkward shape and size, two people are required to move plasterboards. A plasterboard should be carried on edge with a person at each end to support it. One person should lead the operation while the other follows instructions from the lead. Care should be taken not to damage the ends of the boards when picking up and setting down, or when negotiating obstacles such as doorways and corridors.

When moving plasterboards outdoors, be aware of the weather conditions as a gust of wind could catch the board and blow you off balance. Try to avoid moving plasterboards in the rain as they are likely to become wet. If this is not possible, limit their exposure to the rain to the absolute minimum, and keep the stack well covered and protected from the wet conditions.

TOOLS AND EQUIPMENT

Once you have established the type of plasterboards to be used, where they are to be installed and how they are to be fixed, you should then gather all the tools and equipment that you will need to carry out the job, taking into account all health and safety and PPE requirements.

Tool	Use
Board knife	Used for cutting boards. Craft knifes can have fixed blades but, for safety reasons, ones with retractable blades are better. Also known as a utility knife.
Tape measure	For measuring accurately. To prevent confusion and mistakes, use tape measures with metric-only scales.
Straight edge or feather edge	For providing a firm and straight guide against which to cut.

Tool	Use
Lath hammer	Used for hammering in plasterboard nails. The broad head ensures that the nail's head is left below the surface of the board without piercing the paper face.
Claw hammer	For extracting nails from the studs and joists or for hammering nails in. Choose a hammer whose weight you are comfortable with.
Drywall driver	For driving in and extracting drywall screws. They come with various voltages but 14.4V or 18V are probably the most practical as they have good power and battery life without being too heavy. Self-loading screw guns are also available.
Surform	Used for smoothing off cut edges or trimming down boards that are slightly too long. Curved cuts can also be formed using this tool. Also known as a rasp or plasterboard plane.
Pad saw	Used for cutting out holes in plasterboards for electrical sockets and pipework, etc. Also used when making complex cuts.
Pencil	Use to mark on adjacent surfaces, the centre of studs and joists, etc. Also used for marking out areas to be cut out or cut off from the plasterboard.

ACCESS EQUIPMENT

When fixing plasterboards to ceiling joists, it is important that the scaffold platform is suitable for the job in hand. Ideally, you want to raise the floor level using staging, ensuring there are no gaps or **traps**, and that the platform is at the correct height for comfortable working.

A platform that is too low will cause you to stretch excessively, which can lead to falls or severe strain injuries. A platform that is too high will cause you to stoop, which again can lead to injury. It is useful to have someone work with you who is of a similar height to yourself. (Refer back to Chapter 1, pages 24–30, for working at height information.)

TYPES OF FIXING FOR PLASTERBOARDS

Plasterboards can be fixed in place using drywall screws or **galvanised** nails, neither of which will rust when plastered over. (A method known as direct bond dry lining, which is covered at Level 2, uses a drywall adhesive to bond the plasterboards directly to a masonry background.)

Plasterboards can be fixed to timber backgrounds with either nails or screws. Since the development of the battery-powered or cordless screwdriver, nail fixing has largely been replaced by screw fixings.

The main reasons for this are that:

- screws offer a more secure fixing than nails and can accommodate some movement in the timber
- there is less chance of damaging the plasterboard when fixing with screws
- it is easier to reposition the boards, should you need to, when using screws
- fewer screw fixings are required.

If nails are to be used, they should be galvanised plasterboard nails or galvanised clouts long enough to go through the board and penetrate the timber by at least:

- 20mm for plasterboards that are 9.5mm thick
- 25mm for plasterboards that are 12.5mm thick or more.

Nails should be fixed every 150mm along the timbers.

When hammering in nails to fix plasterboards, care needs to be taken not to miss the nail. Missing the nail will result in you delivering a hard hammer blow to the plasterboard itself, damaging and weakening its plaster core.

Traps

Where the end of a scaffold board on a scaffold or working platform has not been correctly supported. When it is walked over the board can give way, causing the person to fall through the resulting gap

Galvanised

A protective zinc coating applied to steel to prevent corrosion or rusting which could cause unsightly staining on the finished plasterboard or cause the fixing to fail

A drywall screw

A plasterboard nail

A galvanised clout nail

Screws need to be **plated drywall screws** that are long enough to penetrate the timber by 25mm. On a wall, they should be spaced 300mm apart along the timbers. On a ceiling, they should be spaced 230mm apart.

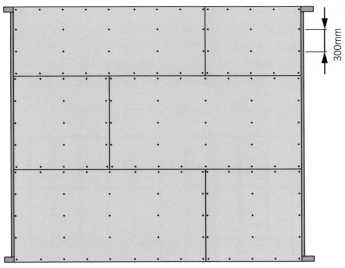

Screw spacing on a plasterboard wall

Plated drywall screw

A screw that has a rust-resistant zinc coating or black phosphate coating. They are sharp pointed and can be used to fix plasterboard to timber or steel channels

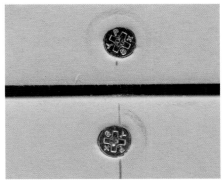

Correctly fixed plasterboard screws

FAULTS WITH FIXED PLASTERBOARDS

A common fault that can occur with plasterboards that are fixed in place with either nails or screws is called 'popping'. This is where the nail or screw fixing has not been secured tightly enough and is sticking out slightly from the face of the plasterboard. This leaves a gap between the back of the plasterboard and the joist or stud into which it is meant to be fixed. If somebody leans on the wall or walks over the joist it will flex, pushing the fixing further forward beyond the face of the plasterboard. A small circle of plaster, the size of the fixing's head, will break loose.

The same fault occurs when the fixing has been tightened too much so that it tears the plasterboard's surface paper and is below the surface face. In this instance, because the paper face has been torn, the strength of the plasterboard is reduced, with only the back sheet of lining paper to hold the weight of the plasterboard.

Both nails and screws should be no closer than 10mm from a bound edge or 13mm from an unbound edge. The heads of the screws should be flush with or slightly denting the surface of the plasterboard without tearing the paper face. Similarly, nails should not tear the paper face of the plasterboard but should sit in a small dent created by the final hammer blow.

Make sure that the fixing, whether it is a nail or a screw, is put in straight. Putting them in at an angle will result in the fixing puncturing the face of the board while protruding from the surface.

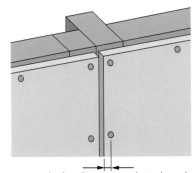

Nail edge distance to plasterboard unbound edges: minimum 13mm bound edges: minimum 10mm

Nail fixings placement

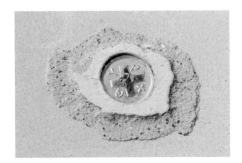

Screw popping

STAGGERING JOINTS

Another common fault that can occur when plasterboards are fixed incorrectly is cracking along the joins. As mentioned in the previous section, when a stud partition wall is leaned on or an upstairs timber floor is walked over, the wooden framework flexes. If a joist or stud had a continuous join where plasterboards meet, running along its length, a crack would develop where the join is. To help prevent this and strengthen the wall, the joins are **staggered**. The following are step-by-step guides for two different plasterboarding scenarios.

Where the first row starts and ends with a full board:

Staggered

Refers to the joint arrangement of plasterboards when they are fixed in place to timber or steel channel backgrounds – the vertical edges should not form a straight line

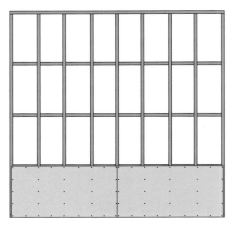

STEP 1 The first row starts and ends with a full board, or as near to it as makes no difference.

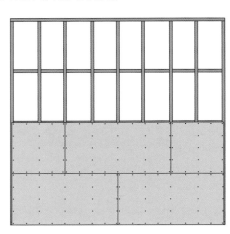

STEP 2 The second row must start and end with a half board.

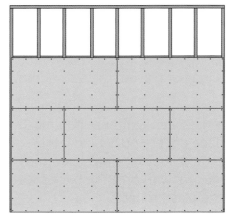

STEP 3 The third row should then be the same as the first.

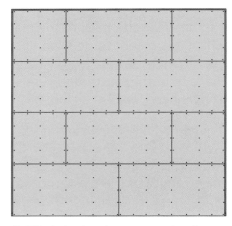

STEP 4 The fourth row must then be as the second. Repeat the pattern until the area is covered.

Where the first row starts with a full board but ends with a half or cut board:

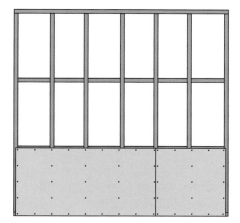

STEP 1 The first row starts with a full board but ends with a half or cut board.

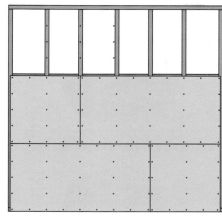

STEP 2 The second row must start with the cut board and end with the full.

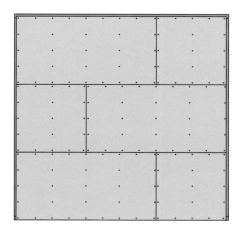

STEP 3 Alternate which end the cut board is positioned for subsequent rows. Repeat the pattern until the area is covered.

Depending on the height of the wall or the width of the ceiling, when fixing the first row of boards it may be necessary to cut them along their length to reduce their width. This will avoid needing to cut a thin length of board for the last row.

MATERIALS USED FOR JOINTING PLASTERBOARD

Staggering the boards will reduce the risk of cracks developing, but this alone is not enough to stop cracks from appearing. The joints also need to be reinforced. There are a number of reinforcing materials that can be used. These include:

- bandage or cotton scrim
- jute or hessian scrim
- self-adhesive fibreglass scrim
- paper tape.

Scrim is an open-weave material that comes in rolls from 50 to 100mm wide and can be stuck over all joints in plasterboard walls and ceilings. It can even be stuck over joints where they meet other walls, such as around the perimeter of the ceiling; here, the scrim needs to be stuck to the plasterboards and then be run or fixed down the walls to reinforce the join.

Scrimming up

Type of scrim	Use
Jute scrim	Jute scrim, although a good reinforcement material, is not often used today.
Cotton or bandage scrim	Bandage or cotton scrim is a thin cotton material. It is applied in the same way as jute scrim and used as reinforcement.
Fibre tape scrim	Self-adhesive fibreglass mesh has largely replaced jute as the scrim of choice for plasterers. As the name suggests, it is self-adhesive so there is no need to first mix and apply plaster to the joints in order to scrim up. In fact, **scrimming up** can take place while the first gauge of plaster is being mixed. Because it is made of fibreglass, it is a strong reinforcement for the joints. It is quick and easy to use and, because of the time saved, it is also economical because it does not need a bag of plaster to apply it. Furthermore, it requires only two applications of finish plaster to cover the scrim; this is known as 'trowel trowel' (which is covered in Chapter 7).

Scrimming up

Applying scrim

Type of scrim	Use
Paper tape 	Paper tape is generally used for reinforcing joints of tapered edged boards, using a process called 'tape and joining', when **dry lining**. The joint between the boards is filled with a joining compound. The paper tape, which is a specially designed paper similar to that used to line plasterboards, is then bedded into the compound. Then, a filler is applied over this to bring the joint flush with the surface of the boards. When the filler has set, it is sanded down before the board work has a coat of primer painted onto it in preparation for decorating. Paper tape is considered the strongest of the jointing materials.

Dry lining

Lining masonry walls with plasterboards by directly bonding them with adhesive, known as 'dot and dab'. The term 'dry lining' comes from the plasterboards being a dry material as opposed to wet plaster

FIXING PLASTERBOARDS TO STUD WALLS

The following steps show you how to fix plasterboards to stud walls.

STEP 1 With a pencil or piece of chalk, mark the centre of each stud onto the ceiling and floor.

STEP 2 To prevent ground moisture from soaking into the plasterboards while they are fixed, place a small piece of doubled-up offcut onto the floor. These are 'packers' that the boards can sit on to keep them off the floor.

STEP 3 Along the base of the wall, measure the distance from the adjacent wall to the centre of the stud closest to (but not longer than) the length of the plasterboard being used. Make a note of this measurement.

STEP 4 From the top of the packers, measure up the wall to the centre of the joint closest to (but not longer than) the width of the plasterboard being used. Make a note of this measurement.

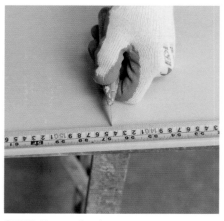

STEP 5 Transfer these measurements to the plasterboard (onto the face without the writing). Check that the cut edge of the plasterboard will be against the adjacent wall. Using your craft knife, make a small incision in the board to indicate the measurements.

STEP 6 Checking the straight edge is lined up with the incision marks, hold the edge firmly and run the knife down the edge, scoring into the plasterboard with the knife.

STEP 7 With your hand, gently tap the back of the board along the cut to break it.

STEP 8 Fold the board in two and run your knife down the inside of the fold to separate the two pieces of plasterboard, taking care not to cut yourself.

STEP 9 Run your surform over the cut edge to smooth off.

INDUSTRY TIP

There is a common saying in construction: 'Measure twice, cut once.' This is a reminder to check your measurements before making any cuts.

STEP 10 Position the plasterboard in place on top of the packers and hold it up with two 'loosely tightened' screws along the top edge to prevent it from falling. Check the board is in the correct position: the side without writing should be on view, the bound edge should be spanning the studs, the cut edge should be at the wall and the uncut edge should be resting squarely on half a stud.

STEP 11 When the board is in the correct position, using a straight edge and the marks on the floor that indicate the studs' centres (see Step 1), draw a pencil line up the board's width to show where each stud's centre is beneath the board.

STEP 12 Once all the studs' centres have been drawn on the board, remove the packers, then, starting from the centre and working outwards, secure the board in place with screw fixings into the centre of each stud, along the board's width. Make sure all screws are now fully tightened.

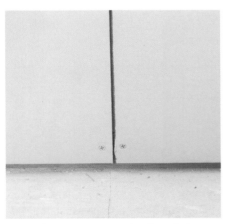

STEP 13 Repeat Steps 2–10 until the bottom row of plasterboards is completed. Take care that they are all in line. Ensure there is a 2–3mm gap between each board: this allows plaster to be squeezed into the gap when the finish coat is applied, strengthening the joint and reducing the risk of cracking.

STEP 14 When measuring and fixing the second row of boards, it is important that boards do not join on the same stud as in the previous row. The joints need to be staggered, which helps minimise the risk of cracking along the joints. Remember to leave a 2–3mm gap between all boards, including between rows.

STEP 15 Repeat Steps 3–10 until the wall is boarded. You will need packers for only the first row.

ACTIVITY

Work out the area of a sheet of plasterboard measuring 2.4m × 1.2m. Then calculate how many sheets of plasterboard would be needed to board the room you are in.

Internal angle

A corner that you can put things in

OUR HOUSE

Select one partition in 'Our House'.

1 From the joist centres, determine the size and fixing for the plasterboard.
2 Sketch out the pattern in which you will fix the plasterboards onto the stud wall.
3 Work out how many fixings you will need (drywall screws or galvanised nails).
4 Determine the length of scrim required to reinforce the joints, **internal angles** and ceiling line.

If the wall you are plasterboarding has electrical boxes fitted – for plug sockets or light switches, for example – gaps for these need to be cut out of the plasterboard before fixing. The following step-by-step guide shows you how to cut out for electrical boxes.

STEP 1 On the wall, measure from where the bottom of the board is going to sit up to the top and bottom of the box.

STEP 2 Transfer these measurements to each end of the plasterboard. Draw a line between these points to give you two parallel horizontal lines.

STEP 3 On the wall, from where one edge of the board is to be situated, measure the distance to each side of the box.

STEP 4 Transfer these measurements to each horizontal line on the plasterboard and draw lines between them to form the outline of the box.

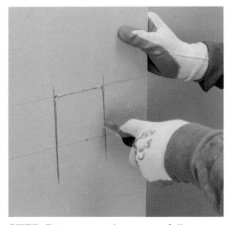

STEP 5 Using a pad saw, carefully cut out the outline, taking care to keep to the lines.

A plasterboarded wall with electrical box fitted

The same method is used to mark the centre of water and central heating pipes that may need to come through the wall, although these can be cut out using either the pad saw or a hole cutting bit.

There are various mechanical lifting aids that you can use to help position plasterboards safely, such as props and hoists.

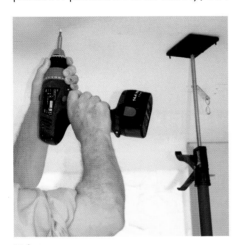

Using a prop

A hoist

FIXING PLASTERBOARDS TO CEILINGS

When fixing plasterboards to ceilings, start at the corner of the room that is the most square. Other than the fact that no packers are required, the process is the same as for walls. Remember:

- make sure joints are staggered

- make sure there is a 2–3mm gap between boards

- make sure that the face of the plasterboard without writing on it is facing out.

PLASTERBOARD WASTE DISPOSAL

Fixing plasterboards is likely to leave you with a lot of offcuts. Some of these will be of use to you (for using as packers, for example) but most will not and should be disposed of regularly, in line with current regulations. Disposing of waste regularly will keep your working area safe, make it easier and quicker for you to work, and you will be less likely to lose tools.

Since 2009, gypsum products such as plasterboards and gypsum-based plasters can no longer be disposed of in landfill sites, because of their high sulphate content. Instead, they have to be disposed of under controlled conditions. Most large- or medium-sized sites separate waste into different skips. Your own college, training centre or employer should also be doing this.

Wherever possible, rather than disposing of waste you should try to reuse it. However, offcuts that are less than 300mm wide and do not span at least three joists/studs should not be used when plasterboarding. To avoid having to use them, plan your job by calculating how many plasterboards long and high the wall (or wide the ceiling) is. It may mean that you have to cut plasterboards to three-quarters of their length or start the first row using half-width boards. Although this is more time consuming and generates more wastage, it results in a far superior job with minimal risk of cracking.

INDUSTRY TIP

Go to the Environment Agency's website (www.environment-agency.gov.uk) for the latest updates on gypsum disposal.

ACTIVITY

Go to the Environment Agency's website and find the latest guidance on disposal of waste. In your own words, summarise the key points of the guidance and your responsibilities as a plasterer.

MEASURING, CUTTING AND FIXING PRE-FORMED BEADS AND EML

Pre-formed beads and EML are used to add strength to plaster and help avoid cracking, especially where different materials meet. EML also helps provide a key to backgrounds.

TOOLS AND EQUIPMENT

Below is a list of the tools and equipment needed to carry out jobs involving pre-formed beads and EML. Look back at pages 166–167 and compare it with the list of tools needed for measuring, cutting and fixing plasterboard.

Tools	Use
Claw hammer	Used for fixing nails.
Tin snips	Used to cut EML and beading.
Cordless screwdriver	Used for fixing screws.
Straight edge	Used for providing a straight guide to cut against.
Drywall driver	Used for driving in and extracting drywall screws.
Tape measure	Used to get accurate measurements.
Staple gun	Used for fixing beads.

Tools		Use
Hawk and trowel		Used for fixing beads with plaster.
Spirit level		Used for checking levels.
PPE		Used for protection when cutting and fitting EML and beads.

EML

Expanded metal lathing, or EML as it now more commonly called, was developed in the mid to late 1800s as an alternative to wooden lathing. Its main benefits are:

- quicker to install than wooden lathing
- improved fireproofing
- compatible with (then newly invented) cements and plasters
- easier to produce curved surfaces
- good as a reinforcement to help prevent cracking.

When EML is used as lathing it still requires three coats of plaster (called **three coat work**) to be applied. But EML's advantages over plasterboards are its durability and its ability to be manipulated onto curved and complex surfaces. It may also be used to reinforce soft, **friable** masonry and provide a key for smooth, dense backgrounds such as concrete.

EML can also be used to clad **structural** steelwork, forming a background for the application of fireproofing materials. On **composite** backgrounds, EML is used to span the joints between different materials, reducing the risk of cracking.

There are two main types of EML in common use as a background for plastering: diamond mesh and rib-lath. In this chapter we will look at diamond mesh EML.

Three coat work

Also known as 'scratch, float and set', this is three distinct layers of plaster. The first coat – the render or scratch – evens out an uneven background. The second coat – the float – provides a true flat surface for the third coat, which is called the set or finish

Friable

Loose, crumbly

Structural

Describing any aspect of a building that forms part of the building's main support

Composite

A wall made up of two or more materials

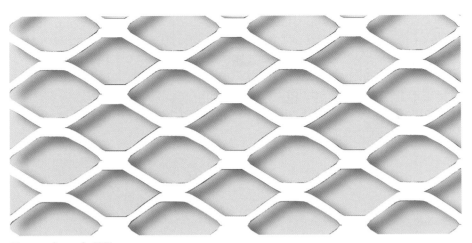

Diamond mesh EML

MEASURING, CUTTING AND FIXING EML

Whichever type of EML you are using, when it is cut to size razor sharp burrs can form. Small pieces of metal can also fly around as you cut them off. Therefore, heavy-duty, tear-resistant gauntlet gloves, long-sleeved overalls and eye protection should be worn at all times when cutting and handling EML, as shown below.

Wearing PPE when cutting EML

When fixing diamond mesh EML to timber backgrounds, the longer length of the diamonds should run across the supports. Cut the EML to length, allowing for the sheets to overlap by 50mm on a supporting timber. Hold the sheet in position with a few well-placed nails or staples that are not fully driven in and allow free movement of the mesh. Then, starting from the centre and working out, use 30mm clout nails or staples to fix the EML into position. Make sure that the mesh is pulled tight in all directions when fixing. This can be done by driving the nails in at an angle, in the direction you want to pull the mesh.

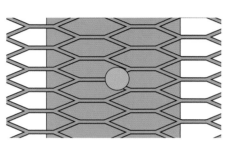

The diamond running against the run of the joist/stud

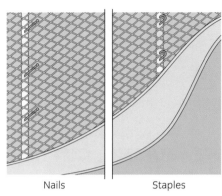

Nails and staples being driven in at an angle

Take care not to overtighten the mesh as it can tear. On the other hand, installing sheets of EML without pulling it tight will result in the sheets sagging or bulging between the timbers. If that happens, when the time comes to apply the plaster, the pressure used in the application will push the sheet of EML behind the line of the timbers. Then, when the trowel is removed, the pressure will be released and the EML will spring forward into its original position, flicking off all the newly applied plaster.

When fixing EML to a steel channel, fixings should be every 100mm along the joist. Overlap each sheet by 25mm along its long edge and 50mm across its width. Support must always be provided across the width of the EML, especially at the end of each sheet. The overlapped joins should be tied together with 1.22mm tie wire.

Another major use for roll or coiled EML is for fixing over timber **wall plates** to create a key. The mesh should be wide enough to cover the timber and at least one course of bricks below it. The EML should be fixed to the timber with nails or staples and to the masonry with screw fixings. Coil EML should be fixed to any other timber members that are found in walls, such as lintels above doors and windows or timber frames with brick infill.

Fixings and tie wires should be made from the same material as the EML. In other words, if you are using galvanised EML then use galvanised fixings and wire; if stainless steel EML is being fitted, stainless steel nails and wire should be used.

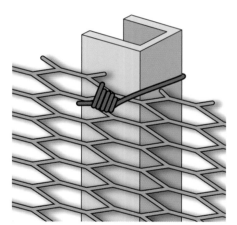

Diamond mesh tied to steel channel

Wall plate

Timber that runs along the top of a wall, to which the roof is fixed

PRE-FORMED BEADS

Before the introduction of pre-formed beads, plasterers would have to form **external angles** and **end stops** using timber profiles (see below). This presented a number of difficulties for the plasterer. The main difficulty was that, when forming an external angle, a profile would need to be set up on one face of the angle while the other face was being plastered. This then had to be reversed to plaster the other face. Angle beads removed the need to do this as, once the bead was fixed in position, both faces of the angle could be worked on at the same time.

Another difficulty overcome by using pre-formed beads is that of producing a neat, clean edge where plasterwork ends. Unless great care was taken, removing the timber profile could damage the finished plaster-work. Stop beads and edging beads are now used to prevent this.

TYPES OF PRE-FORMED BEADS

Like EML, beads are manufactured from stainless steel and galvanised steel. More recently a comprehensive range of uPVC beads have come onto the market, some of which are coloured to match modern **through colour external finishes**.

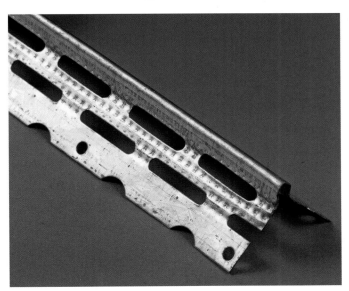
Metal beads

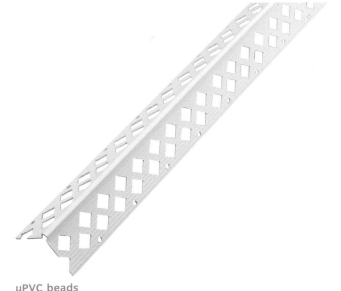
uPVC beads

There is an extensive range of beads available from various manufacturers in lengths of 2.4m and 3m. Some of these are covered at Level 2; in this chapter we will look at:

- angle beads

- stop beads.

External angle

A reveal or return of a wall forming a right angle and a corner

End stop

The neat edge where plasterwork stops

Timber profiles

Through colour external finish

Also known as 'coloured render', this is a pre-mixed external plaster that comes in a range of colours

ACTIVITY

Go to a manufacturer's website or contact a supplier and list as many types of available beads and their uses as you can.

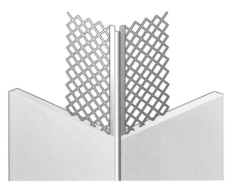

A standard angle bead

Arris

The very tip of an external angle

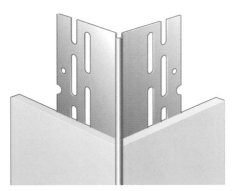

A thin coat angle bead

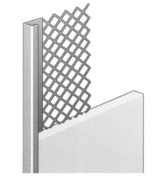

A stop bead

Fixing a stop bead

Standard angle beads

As with many things in plastering, you will notice that there are many terms and names for the same thing. Beads are no exception. Standard angle beads are also known as rough coat beads, floating beads, wide mesh beads and by various other names depending on the manufacturer and regional differences.

These beads are used to form a clean, neat **arris** around window openings, door openings, chimney breasts and other external angles where two or three coat plasterwork is to be carried out. When the bead is fixed, it will allow plaster to be applied up to 13mm thick, including a float coat and a set.

Whether using galvanised, stainless steel or uPVC beads, the method of installation is basically the same. However, if in doubt, the manufacturer's data sheets should be checked for specific instructions.

Thin coat angle beads

Thin coat angle beads, as with other beads, are known by different names by different manufacturers and in different regions. You may hear them called board beads, drywall beads, skimming beads or setting beads.

They are used when one coat plastering is required, such as on plasterboards or poured in situ concrete. Because they are used to give a neat working edge for finish plaster, which is only 2–3mm thick, it is not possible to plumb these beads. Any plumbing of walls will need to be done before fixing the beads. Thin coat angle beads can be fixed with galvanised nails, drywall screws, dabs of plaster or staples.

Thin coat beads are available for finish plasters 3mm and 6mm thick.

Stop beads

Stop beads are a useful means of giving a neat edge to plaster. For example, where more than one surface finish or material is required, a stop bead can be used to define each separate area. Stop beads can also be fixed when plastering up to an external angle but not going round it. They may also be used to build up features, like raised or sunken panels.

Standard stop beads come in lengths of 2.4m and 3m and for plaster thicknesses of 10mm, 13mm, 16mm and 19mm. They may be galvanised for interior plasters and stainless steel for exterior work.

STORING AND HANDLING PRE-FORMED BEADS

Beads made from thin sheet metal that is formed and pressed into the required shape are easily damaged by mishandling or poor storage. Angle beads should always be stored flat, in racks or off the ground, and supported along their length. Storing beads upright for any length of time is not recommended as they will bow under their own weight.

Once a bead has bent, especially an angle bead, it is very difficult if not impossible to fix that bead so that it is straight again. Even if you manage to get it in position so it is plumb and straight, as the plaster dabs dry the bead will bend back to its curved shape, leaving you with a corner that is completely misaligned. When handling beads, take them from the rack carefully and carry them with two hands.

MEASURING, CUTTING AND FIXING PRE-FORMED BEADS

Pre-formed beads can be fixed by nails, screws, staples or even plaster itself, depending on the background.

Measuring and fixing beads to stud walling is fairly straightforward. The following steps show how this is done.

STEP 1 Measure the angle.

STEP 2 Transfer this measurement to the angle bead and mark across the nose with a pencil.

STEP 3 With a junior hacksaw, cut through the nosing of the bead. Next, use snips to cut through the mesh wings, up to the hacksaw cut.

STEP 4 Push the bead tight into the arris of the board and fix in place.

Be careful not to over-tighten fixing screws as they will pull the bead out of line and bend it. Similarly, if you use nails to attach the bead, make sure you do not hit the bead with the hammer as this will dent the bead.

Place a fixing every 600mm or until there is no movement in the bead and the head of the fixing is tight enough to receive an adequate covering of plaster. Make sure the bead nosing is correctly aligned with the arris.

When fixing beads to steel channels, you should also use drywall screws.

Beads fixed to plasterboards that require a finish coat of plaster and have been fixed by direct bond dry lining need to be secured in place with plaster. This is because there are no timbers to fix the nails into! Apply dabs of finish plaster to each side of the angle and fix the bead as described above for standard angle beads, only instead of plumbing the bead ensure it is pressed tight to and in line with the arris. Fixing beads to concrete is done in the same way, but make sure the concrete has been prepared correctly as described in Chapter 3.

If the angle to which you are fixing the bead is longer than the bead, it is possible to create longer beads by joining them together, known as extending beads. This is done by inserting a clout nail with its head cut off into the back of the nosing and gently bending the back to hold it in place. When the bead is fixed in position, ensure the join is flush – you should be able to run a finger over the join without feeling it.

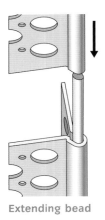

Extending bead

Case Study: Florence

Florence was asked by her supervisor to fix plasterboards and apply a finish coat of plaster to the bathrooms of a new development. She was given the relevant drawings and specifications for the job. These stated that the ceiling should be boarded with 12.5mm standard plasterboards, using screw fixings. All stud walls required moisture-resistant plasterboards to be fixed and all plasterboards, ceilings and walls were to receive a 3mm plaster finish coat.

When Florence read the specification, she remembered a recent lesson at college that had covered compatibility and how it was recommended that moisture-resistant plasterboards don't have plaster directly applied to them without first being treated with a bonding agent. She brought her concerns to her supervisor's attention.

After the architect and client were consulted, it was decided that since the stud walls were far enough away from the wet areas, the moisture-resistant plasterboards could be replaced with standard plasterboards. This saved the developer the extra cost of the more expensive moisture-resistant plasterboards as well as the expense – both in money and to their reputation – by not having to carry out any remedial work in putting right this mistake.

Work through the following questions to check your learning.

1 Which one of the following is a standard thickness of plasterboard?

a 10mm.

b 10.5mm.

c 12mm.

d 12.5mm.

2 What is EML an abbreviation for?

a External metal lathing.

b Expensive metal lathing.

c Expanded metal lathing.

d Exposed metal lathing.

3 The use of plasterboard in construction

a speeds up the build process

b increases drying time

c reduces waste

d is no longer practised.

4 Which one of the following tools is used for cutting EML?

a Lath hammer.

b Craft knife.

c Tin snips.

d Scissors.

5 What is the minimum length for screws to fix 9.5mm plasterboards?

a 25mm.

b 32mm.

c 38mm.

d 40mm.

6 Plasterboards are 'staggered'

a to reduce wastage

b only on ceilings

c for ease of installation

d to reduce the risk of cracking.

7 How far apart should screws be when fixing 12.5mm plasterboards to timber stud walls?

a 250mm.

b 300mm.

c 425mm.

d 500mm.

8 When fixing EML with nails, the nails should be

a 50mm long

b driven in at an angle

c spaced at 300mm centres

d driven in straight.

9 Impact-resistant plasterboards would be best suited for

a garage ceilings

b bathroom walls

c school corridors

d exterior walls.

10 What is applied to plasterboard joints to prevent cracking?

a EML.

b Plaster.

c Beads.

d Scrim.

11 When fixing EML to internal timber backgrounds, it is important to

   a   keep it tight

   b   use stainless steel EML

   c   use screw fixings

   d   leave a gap between sheets.

12 Nails used for fixing sheet materials are galvanised to prevent

   a   nail popping

   b   rusting

   c   accidents

   d   dropping them.

13 Which one of the following is not a type of bead?

   a   Thin coat stop.

   b   Standard stop.

   c   Render stop.

   d   Thin render stop.

14 Beads should be stored in such a way so as to prevent them

   a   drying

   b   freezing

   c   shrinking

   d   bending.

15 When cutting plasterboards, a ragged edge indicates it is

   a   cut in the wrong direction

   b   an out-of-date plasterboard

   c   time to change the pad saw's blade

   d   a moisture-resistant board.

16 A 2–3mm gap should be left between plasterboards to

   a   make installation easier

   b   allow for expansion of boards

   c   reduce the risk of cracking

   d   allow for movement of timbers.

17 The **best** way to fix angle beads to plasterboard-clad timber backgrounds is to use

   a   tie wire

   b   galvanised clout nails

   c   board finish plaster

   d   self-adhesive scrim.

18 What is the colour of fire-resistant plasterboard?

   a   Blue.

   b   Pink.

   c   Green.

   d   Grey.

19 What tools are used to cut angle bead?

   a   Tin snips and straight edge.

   b   Hacksaw and spirit level.

   c   Spirit level and straight edge.

   d   Hacksaw and tin snips.

20 What is a common thickness of a thin coat stop bead?

   a   2mm.

   b   3mm.

   c   4mm.

   d   5mm.

Chapter 6
Unit 124: Applying floating coats to walls

When applying plaster to solid backgrounds and lathing, the quality of the finished plasterwork depends largely on how well the floating coat has been applied. It is the floating coat that determines how plumb and flat the finished surface will be.

You must, therefore, know how a good floating coat is achieved and be able to put this knowledge into practice. Being able to achieve an accurately plumb and flat surface requires different techniques depending on the standards and materials specified.

By reading this chapter you will know how to:

1 Apply floating coats to walls.

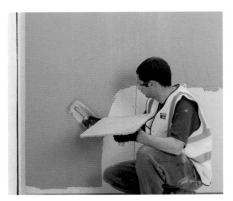

Setting coat

Float and set

Scratch, float and set

ACTIVITY

Go online and research different grades of backing plaster used for floating coats.

WHAT IS A FLOATING COAT?

Plasterwork applied to internal solid backgrounds or lathing is a combination of a number of different layers. The combinations can be summarised as follows:

- *Set finish or setting coat*: This is one coat work where a thin setting coat of plaster is applied in two applications to either plasterboard or some in situ poured concrete backgrounds

- *Float and set*: This is two coat work where a thicker backing coat plaster, known as the floating coat, is applied to masonry backgrounds that are plumb and in good condition, such as new blockwork. The floating coat provides a suitable background for the setting coat

- *Scratch, float and set*: This is three coat work where a masonry background is in poor condition, not plumb and straight or is made up of a number of different materials, known as a composite background. A scratch coat of plaster must first be applied to the background. This will provide a suitable background for a floating coat to be applied to, followed by the set.

This means that the floating coat can either be:

- the first coat of plaster in two coat work (float and set) on even straight backgrounds such as blocks and bricks

- the second coat of plaster in three coat work (scratch, float and set) on uneven backgrounds such as old brick or stone.

The floating coat forms the flat surface base for the setting coat. Because the setting coat is only approximately 2–3mm thick, any defects or deviations from a flat surface in the floating coat will be difficult to conceal. As a result, the floating coat has to be flat, plumb and even with no hollows, bulges or high points across its surface.

TOOLS AND EQUIPMENT

To achieve a flat, true surface there are a number of procedures that have to be followed. These procedures are carried out using the tools in the following table. For more information on these tools, refer back to Chapter 4, pages 138–140.

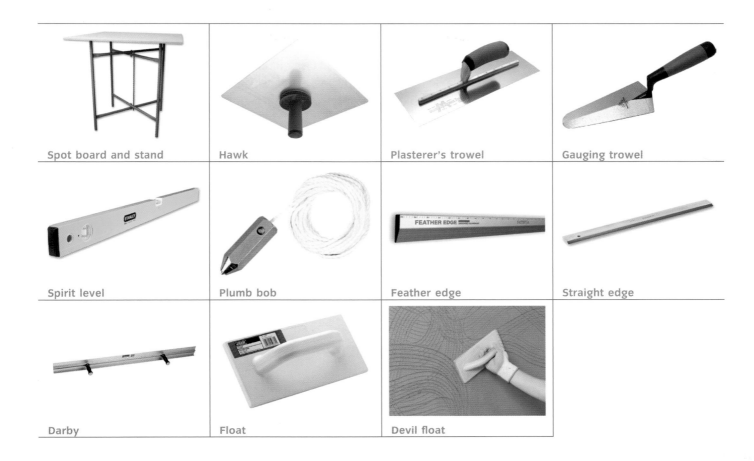

Spot board and stand	Hawk	Plasterer's trowel	Gauging trowel
Spirit level	Plumb bob	Feather edge	Straight edge
Darby	Float	Devil float	

MATERIALS USED FOR FLOATING COATS

The floating coat is a backing plaster which is applied approximately 10–12mm thick. Backing plaster is made up of an **aggregate**, the inert filler that makes up the bulk of the mix, combined with a **binder** that sets and holds the aggregate together. It is the size and type of aggregate, along with type and amount of binder used, that give the plaster its strength. There are various grades of backing plaster on the market used for floating coats such as Thistle Bonding Coat, Thistle Hardwall and Thistle Tough Coat. Setting times for these plasters is between one-and-a-half and two hours.

We will also look at different additives used in floating coat plaster mixes later in this section.

AGGREGATES

Perlite

Perlite is a naturally occurring mineral that is mined, then crushed and heated. When it is heated, it expands up to 20 times its original size in much the same way that corn kernels expand to make popcorn. Expanded perlite resembles polystyrene beads in appearance, with similar insulating properties. Expanded perlite also has good fire resistance properties.

Aggregate

A 'filler', aggregate makes up the bulk of a mix. The size and type of aggregate are what determine the mix's strength

Binder

The binder is the active ingredient in a mix. It sets and holds the aggregate and other materials together

Perlite

Expanded vermiculite

Expanded vermiculite

Like perlite, vermiculite is a naturally occurring mineral that is mined then crushed and heated. Vermiculite will expand up to 30 times its original size and resembles a concertina. It too has very good thermal insulating and fireproofing properties.

Sand

The sand used for floating coats should be well-graded, sharp sand. This type of sand has angular grains and is able to pass through a sieve with a 5mm mesh size. The term 'well-graded' means that the sizes of the grains of sand range from 5mm down to fine particles. The gaps or voids between the larger grains of sand are filled by the smaller grains.

The finest particles, known as 'fines', are made up of silt and clay. They fill the gap between the smaller grains of sand, which helps lubricate them, and help the binder to coat the sand particles. Good plastering sand should have no more than 5–10% fines. Refer back to Chapter 3, page 120, to see an illustration of sand particles.

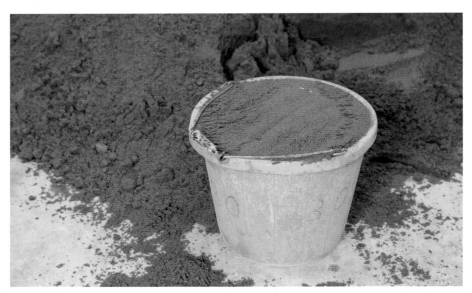
Sand

Up to 4% of the fines can be clay: any more than this can cause problems with bulking, where the clay soaks up more water than is required and swells up, increasing the volume of the sand. If this happens, when the plaster dries out it will shrink excessively, causing cracking and hollows to appear. But if there is not enough clay in the fines then the sand will not retain water, making it difficult to work with as it dries out quickly.

Sand that is not well-graded – called 'uniform' sand – has grains that are all the same size. Because the gaps between the grains are not filled with a range of differently sized grains, more binder has to be added to fill the voids. Binder is more expensive than sand, so this puts up the cost of plastering. It will also lead to problems with shrinkage and cracking.

ACTIVITY

Carry out a sieve test on a sample of sand by passing a known quantity of sand through a series of increasingly smaller mesh sieves, starting with 5mm, then 4mm, 3mm, 2mm, 1mm and finally 0.5mm. For each sieve, calculate the percentage of particles left behind.

The following steps show you how to carry out a silt test.

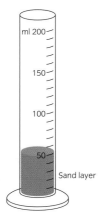

STEP 1 Put sand in a measuring cylinder until it reaches the 50ml mark.

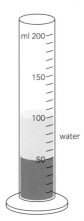

STEP 2 Pour water in. Fill the measuring cylinder to the 100ml mark.

STEP 3 Add a teaspoon of salt and stir well.

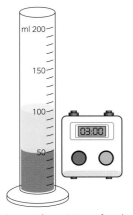

STEP 4 Leave the mixture for three hours to settle. The silt will separate from the sand.

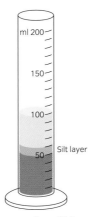

STEP 5 Measure the silt layer and calculate its percentage of the total volume of sand.

ACTIVITY

Carry out a silt test as described in the steps and calculate the percentage of silt in the sand tested.

BINDERS

The following are binders used in floating coats, which set and hold the aggregates together.

Gypsum

Gypsum is a widespread and naturally occurring soft rock containing calcium sulphate. The gypsum rock is mined, then crushed and heated during which it undergoes a chemical change. It is then milled to a fine powder, producing a class A **hemihydrate** plaster. When water is added, the reverse chemical reaction takes place: the gypsum crystallises and sets, giving off the hydration heat used in its manufacture. When it has cooled the plaster has fully set.

The **setting time** for class A plaster is approximately 20 minutes so in order to cover large areas the setting time needs to be extended. This is done during manufacture by adding **retarders**, changing the plaster from a class A hemihydrate to a class B retarded hemihydrate that takes longer to set.

Hemihydrate

Where a substance's natural water content has been reduced by 50–75%

Setting time

The time between mixing cement or gypsum plaster with water and the mixture starting to harden

Retarder

A chemical additive that slows down the setting time of gypsum plasters and cement

ACTIVITY

Using a search engine, find an online copy of *The Thistle plaster selector guide*. Investigate the setting times of the Thistle range of products.

Raw gypsum

Shale

A fine-grained rock that is formed from consolidated clay, quartz and calcite and that can be split into fragile pieces

Rotary kiln

A large kiln that is set at an angle. The heat source is at the bottom of the kiln so it is cooler towards the top. As the whole kiln rotates, the limestone and clay mixture inside travels through it

Cement

Cement is made up of 75% chalk or limestone and 25% clay or **shale**. These are ground down to produce a fine powder. With the addition of a small amount of water, the mixture is fired in a **rotary kiln** at a temperature of 1700°c. This makes the limestone and clay bond together, changing their chemical make-up. This is then milled to a fine powder, with the addition of 1–5% of raw gypsum. Known as Ordinary Portland Cement (OPC), it has an initial setting time of no less than 45 minutes and a final set of no more than 10 hours.

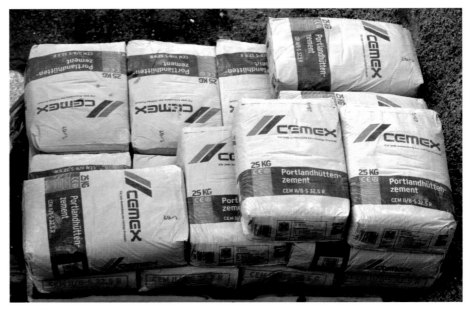

Bagged cement

INDUSTRY TIP

Hydrated lime works as a plasticiser in a sand–lime cement mortar mix, making the mix more plastic and workable.

ACTIVITY

Go online and look up 'lime slaking' or 'slaking lime' to discover what this is.

Lime

Lime has been used in construction for thousands of years. Before the invention of cement and for some time afterwards, construction projects were carried out using lime as the binder in mortars and plasters. The vast majority of housing stock built as recently as the middle of the 20th century was built using lime mortar to lay the bricks and lime plaster to cover the walls and ceilings.

Lime is made from limestone, an abundant rock that is quarried, then crushed and heated, changing its chemical make-up to produce a useable binder. When lime sets, it turns back to limestone. This is known as the 'lime cycle'.

Lime can be a dangerous material, causing serious burns if it comes into contact with your skin or eyes. When working with lime, always use the full range of PPE.

Limestone to be quarried

ADDITIVES

When using sand cement mixes, there are a number of additives that can be introduced to alter its characteristics. (Pre-mixed gypsum backing plasters do not need additives added by plasterers. Any additives needed to give each plaster its specific characteristic will have been added during the manufacturing process. All you need to do is add the plaster to the required amount of water. The manufacturer's instructions regarding mixing and application should be followed at all times.)

The additives that can be added to sand cement mixes include the following.

Plasticiser

Plasticiser
Commonly sold as a liquid in 5l bottles, although powder versions are also available, plasticisers are mixed into the gauging water. They improve the workability of a sand cement mix. When using a plasticiser, always follow the manufacturer's instructions carefully.

Hydrated lime
Hydrated lime acts as a plasticiser. It also reduces the risk of cracking and provides suction for subsequent coats.

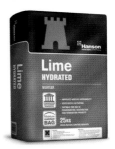
Hydrated lime

Waterproofer
As the name suggests, when a waterproofer is added to a sand cement mix, the resulting coat of plaster when set is resistant to water. This characteristic is very useful in shower blocks, swimming pools and other locations where water is present, preventing the water from soaking into the wall.

Waterproofer

Care should be taken with its use, however, as it will also prevent water from coming out of a wall. For instance, if the inside of a cellar is coated with waterproof plaster, the cellar will remain dry as the surrounding ground water is prevented from entering the room. But the water will still be entering the walls of the cellar before becoming 'trapped' inside the wall. Unless it is able to escape, the water builds up in the brickwork and will eventually blow the plaster due to the pressure, possibly damaging the brickwork, too.

DIFFERENT TYPES OF MIXES FOR FLOATING COATS

Whether you are applying the floating coat onto a scratch coat for three coat work, or directly onto masonry, concrete, plasterboard or other suitable backgrounds for two coat work, there are two major factors to take into consideration.

- *Compatibility*: Is the plaster material compatible with the background or is it going to have an adverse effect? For example, a plaster that has high lime content is unsuitable for applying onto plasterboard as it will not adhere.

- *Strength*: When choosing which plaster or mix ratio to use, it is important that the plaster is not stronger than the background to which it is to be applied. For instance, a dense, hard background such as concrete, engineering bricks and some stones are perfectly capable of coping with having a strong 4:1 sand cement mix applied to them. But if this mix was used as a floating coat on lightweight aerated blocks, as the mix dries and shrinks the strength of it would cause the plaster to crack, blow and **delaminate**. In some extreme cases, it has been known for blocks to crack as a result of too strong a mix being used. A pre-mixed gypsum-based backing plaster would be the better option here, depending upon the conditions it will be exposed to. Alternatively, a weaker sand–lime–cement mix at 6:1:1 or even 9:2:1 could be used.

Chapter 3 gives information about some common backgrounds for floating coats and the most appropriate backing plaster and mix to use. This will help you decide the most suitable plaster to use. However, each background should be assessed on an individual basis.

Delaminate

To divide or become divided into layers. It indicates a failure of composite materials

INDUSTRY TIP

When using sand, cement and/or lime for plastering, it is important to **gauge** the mixes. This will ensure the mix strength is consistent.

Gauge

To measure

The most commonly used undercoat solid plasters in industry are Hardwall, Tough coat, Browning and Bonding. The table below shows examples of these plasters by British Gypsum; other manufacturers such as Knauf and Lafarge also make backing plaster.

| Plaster | What is the background surface?
←— High ——— Suction ——— Low —→ | | | | | | | | |
	Aircrete blocks	Common bricks	Medium-density blocks	Dense blocks	Engineering bricks with raked joints	Plasterboard and Glasroc F Multiboard	Cast in situ and pre-cast concrete	Painted/tiled surfaces	Metal lathing
Thistle Hardwall High impact resistance for most masonry backgrounds. Can be spray applied.				Not on smooth low-suction blocks					When bridging columns and lintels
Thistle Tough Coat High coverage for most masonry backgrounds. Can be spray applied.				Not on smooth low-suction blocks					When bridging columns and lintels
Thistle Browning For solid backgrounds with adequate key.	Use G in extreme cases								
Thistle Bonding Coat For smooth and low-suction backgrounds.				Use B on smooth low-suction blocks		Use B on MR boards	Use B	Use B	

APPLYING FLOATING COATS

Whichever plaster you are using, and regardless of whether you are applying the floating coat to a scratch coat, directly onto block/brickwork or even onto plasterboards, the process is basically the same.

First, work out what materials to use, making sure they are compatible with the background onto which they are to be applied, and then prepare the background accordingly.

To float a wall that contains no features such as doorways or window openings, you can use one of three methods. The method used will depend on the quality and accuracy of the finished work required. You can use:

1 the plumb dot and screed method

2 the broad screed method

3 or the free hand method.

You will find details about the desired quality and accuracy, and the method to be used, in the job specification. (See Chapter 1, page 51 for more details about specifications.)

PLUMB DOT AND SCREED

The most accurate method for applying floating coats is called plumb dot and screed. This is where strips of plaster, known as screeds, are applied to the wall plumb and at convenient intervals. When the screeds are firm enough, the area of the wall between the screeds has plaster applied to it and, using the screeds as guides, the excess plaster is ruled off so the whole wall area is flush with the screeds, producing a perfectly plumb and flat wall.

The following steps show you how to apply floating coats using the plumb dot and screed method.

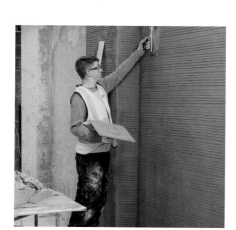

STEP 1 Apply a dab of plaster approximately 150–300mm from the ceiling and adjacent wall.

STEP 2 Set the dot into it. The distance from the wall surface to face of the dot will be the thickness of the floating coat.

STEP 3 Directly below the top dot, set another dot approximately 300mm from the floor.

STEP 4 Check that the dots are plumb.

STEP 5 When the dots have stiffened, apply plaster material between them to form the screeds.

STEP 6 Using the floating rule or feather edge, rule off the excess plaster between the dots.

STEP 7 Fill any hollows. Repeat Steps 6 and 7 until the screed is flush with the dots and free from hollows.

STEP 8 When the screeds have stiffened sufficiently, consolidate the surface with a float and form key with a devil float. Remember to remove the dots and fill in with stiffening floating material.

STEP 9 Apply plaster between the screeds, starting at the top of the wall and working **heel** to **toe**.

STEP 10 Repeat Step 9 until you reach the bottom screed.

STEP 11 Place the thinner edge of the rule across both screeds and, using a side-to-side motion, draw the edge up the screeds, ensuring that the edge remains in contact with both screeds at all times.

Heel

The back of a laying on trowel's blade

STEP 12 Any excess plaster will gather on the edge of the rule. This should be cleaned off the edge and returned to the spot.

Toe

The front of a laying on trowel's blade

STEP 13 Fill any hollows until the plaster is flush with the screeds and all hollows are filled.

STEP 14 Repeat these steps until the area between the screeds is completely covered and ruled off.

STEP 15 The finished look.

BROAD SCREED

Although using plumbed dots and screeds is the most accurate way of floating a wall, it is time consuming and therefore expensive so is generally reserved for high-specification work. The method generally used on site is the broad screed method. When using this method, particular attention should be paid to all the internal angles. If these are not correct, this will be an obvious defect that will need correcting.

Broad screed wall

The following steps show you how to apply floating coats using the broad screed method.

STEP 1 Form the first screed up to 500mm wide, applying plaster to the right-hand side of the wall from the ceiling to 25mm short of the floor/DPC and approximately at the required thickness.

STEP 2 Rule this off, checking it is plumb and filling hollows, etc.

STEP 3 Apply a second screed along the ceiling line.

STEP 4 Rule in the ceiling line.

STEP 5 Apply another screed 25mm short of the floor/DPC.

STEP 6 Apply the floating coat between the screeds and rule off. Take care not to scoop out the screeds as they will still be soft.

STEP 7 Ruling in.

Before you apply your floating coat to the blockwork in 'Our House', draw the dot and screed system on the walls in the bathroom and show the procedure in steps.

Explain why you would use this system instead of broad screed in the bathroom, unlike other rooms in the house.

FREE HAND METHOD

The third way of applying floating coats is the free hand method. Instead of using dots and screeds or broad screeds as a guide, the plaster is simply ruled off and straightened with a straight edge. This is a method used by experienced plasterers who are confident with using the straight edge rule. When the plaster material is firm enough, a devil float is passed over it to give a key. This is in preparation for the skim coat.

FLOATING UP PLASTER MATERIALS

Plaster surfaces are left rough after the backing plaster has been ruled off because aggregates in the mix are dragged apart by the action of the rule over the surface. This effect can be reduced by tilting the floating rule back slightly when ruling off. Using a darby on lightweight gypsum plaster will close in the surface when it is passed over.

However, with both methods there is a need for the surface to be **consolidated**. This is when any misses and minor lumps and bumps are filled and flattened out to create a smoother surface onto which to apply the setting coat. It is carried out using a float, generally made from polyurethane.

When the plaster material has sufficiently stiffened, place the face of the float flat to the wall and, using a figure-of-eight pattern, rub the surface up. The plaster material should be stiff enough so that there are no drag marks left behind by the float but soft enough to flatten any high spots and fill in the low spots. Any misses can be filled with stiffening material and rubbed flush.

Consolidate/consolidated

To close in the surface of a floating coat or floor screed with a float, making it more dense and compact

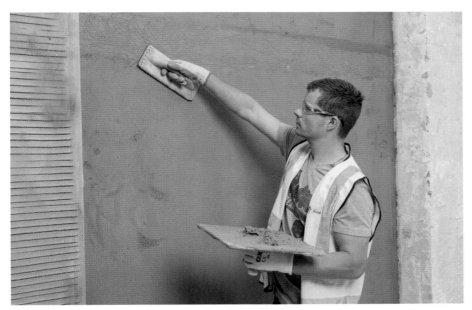

Consolidating the surface

In the internal angles, the float should be worked back and forth along the angle. Ensure that the ceiling and adjacent walls have been cleaned of any plaster material that may have accumulated there. To prevent a hollow being rubbed into the wall, keep the float moving over the wall and avoid using a purely circular motion.

Drag marks

Clearing accumulated plaster

DEVILLING A FLOATING COAT

A devil float is a tool used to provide a key for a setting coat of plaster. It is a plastic float with nails hammered through the top of one end so they stick through the face by 1mm.

Immediately after floating up has been completed, use the devil float in a figure-of-eight pattern to key the surface of the wall ready to receive a setting coat.

A keyed surface

Devilling a floating coat

OUR HOUSE

Work out the amount of floating coat plaster required to plaster the living room walls in 'Our House' by working through the tasks below. Note that you can choose the type of floating coat plaster for these tasks.

1   Measure the perimeter of the room and multiply by the height. This will give you the overall surface area to be plastered in m².
2   Measure all window and door openings by multiplying their length by their breadth. Deduct this measurement from the surface area calculated in Task 1.
3   Now that you have the total measurement in m², work out how much floating coat plaster you require to float the walls. You can do this by dividing the amount of bag coverage by the surface area calculated in Task 2, working to the nearest full bag.
4   When you have calculated the amount of bagged floating coat plaster required, work out the cost. Don't forget to add 10% to allow for wastage.

REPAIRING AND MAKING GOOD

When repairing or making good two coat plasterwork, there are important points to remember.

1   Carefully remove all damaged plaster and cut back to a sound area.

2   Prepare the surface by brushing it clean and dampening it down.

3   Mix appropriate plaster for the background. Whether it is a high- or low-suction background will determine the grade of backing plaster.

4   Apply the plaster to the wall.

5   Using a straight edge, rule off the floating coat so it is level with the existing work.

6   Carefully cut back the edge of the floating coat, allowing 2mm clearance for the skimming coat.

7   Use a devil float to key the surface.

8   Clean the work area before applying the finish plaster.

9   When applying the finish plaster coat, take great care to make sure the new plaster does not gather onto the original work.

10   The final surface should be flush, smooth and free from blemishes.

INDUSTRY TIP

Remember the importance of properly preparing for plastering – see Chapter 3 for more information.

INDUSTRY TIP

When making good, make sure the backing plaster is compatible with the background.

Case Study: Howard

Howard is a young trainee plasterer who was been asked to make good a wall. The wall to be repaired was 2m high and 1.4m wide. Although Howard had fixed plasterboard and applied finish plaster before, this was his first attempt at applying a floating coat. The background surface to be repaired was smooth concrete.

Howard correctly calculated how much plaster he would need. He checked that the original plasterwork was sound and prepared the surface, then mixed the backing plaster. Howard applied the plaster and, using a straight edge, ruled off the wall. He carefully cut back the edge of the floating coat, allowing 2mm clearance for the skimming coat. Howard cleaned the work area and went home.

Howard came in to work the following morning and found that the wall had blown (ie come away from the wall). He went to find the foreman who had a look and asked Howard: 'Did you prepare the background by brushing the surface?' Howard replied: 'Yes, I did.' The foreman then asked: 'What grade of backing plaster did you use?' Howard pointed to the red bag and said: 'Hardwall.'

Immediately, the foreman knew this was the wrong grade of plaster. For smooth concrete backgrounds the correct grade of backing plaster is bonding. This comes in a purple bag.

Although Howard had prepared the background surface correctly, because he had used the wrong plaster he had to remove it all and start the job again using the correctly specified backing plaster.

Work through the following questions to check your learning.

1   Which grade of lightweight backing plaster should be used on plasterboard?

   a   Browning.

   b   Tough coat.

   c   Bonding.

   d   Hardwall.

2   Which one of the following tools should be used to key a floating coat?

   a   Gauging trowel.

   b   Devil float.

   c   Spirit level.

   d   Plasterer's trowel.

3   Which one of the following is an aggregate found in lightweight plaster?

   a   Perlite.

   b   Lime.

   c   Cement.

   d   Sand.

4   Before skimming onto a floating coat

   a   the angles should always be cut out

   b   an internal angle trowel should be used

   c   a cross grain float should be used

   d   a comb scratcher should be used.

5   Which one of the following tools should be used to check a wall is plumb?

   a   Spirit level.

   b   Float.

   c   Darby.

   d   Trowel.

6   On which material would a silt test be performed?

   a   Plaster.

   b   Sand.

   c   Lime.

   d   Vermiculite.

7   What is the approximate thickness of a floating coat?

   a   2–4mm.

   b   4–6mm.

   c   10–12mm.

   d   14–16mm.

8   What will happen if the background is **not** compatible with the backing plaster?

   a   Plaster will stay wet.

   b   Plaster will crack.

   c   Plaster will set too slowly.

   d   Plaster will fall off immediately.

9   Which one of the following is **not** a method used when floating a wall?

   a   Broad screed.

   b   Plumb dot and screed.

   c   Free hand.

   d   Trowel float trowel.

10 Which one of the following should be used when ruling off the floating coat?

   a   Straight edge.

   b   Spirit level.

   c   Plasterer's trowel.

   d   Float.

11 Which of the following is a low-suction background?

a   Thermalite block.

b   Plasterboard.

c   Common brick.

d   Fletton brick.

12 Which one of these materials is an aggregate in a sand, lime and cement mix?

a   Lime.

b   Cement.

c   Sand.

d   Vermiculite.

13 Which one of these materials is a binder in a sand and cement mix?

a   Cement.

b   Sand.

c   Vermiculite.

d   Perlite.

14 Which one of the following materials should be well-graded and sharp?

a   Lime.

b   Plaster.

c   Sand.

d   Cement.

15 Which one of the following is a binder in a lightweight backing plaster?

a   Plaster.

b   Lime.

c   Vermiculite.

d   Perlite.

16 What must be done to a wall before making good?

a   Apply a screed.

b   Prepare the background.

c   Determine labour cost.

d   Clean tools.

17 Which tool is used to spread plaster?

a   Trowel.

b   Bucket trowel.

c   Water brush.

d   Hawk.

18 What is the class of retarded hemihydrate plaster used for floating coats?

a   Class A.

b   Class B.

c   Class C.

d   Class D.

19 Which of the following is the correct setting time for bonding grade backing plaster?

a   1½–2 hours.

b   2½–3 hours.

c   3½–4 hours.

d   4½–5 hours.

20 What is the approximate thickness of setting plaster applied to a floating coat?

a   5–6mm.

b   4–5mm.

c   3–4mm.

d   2–3mm.

Chapter 7
Unit 125: Applying setting coats to walls

This chapter looks at the correct way of applying and finishing setting coats to a variety of backgrounds. It is a mistake to consider the setting coat to be the most important: each coat of plaster or process followed is equally important in its own right and will have a direct influence over the quality of the finish. However, because the setting coat is the finished product, the quality of the finish achieved is the primary aspect on which you will be judged.

By reading this chapter you will know how to:

1   Apply setting coats to walls.

WHAT IS A SETTING COAT?

As explained in the previous chapters in this book, the type of plaster used depends on the type of background to which it is applied and on the conditions that it will be subjected to. Setting coats are no different: they must be compatible.

You should also be aware that many things in plastering have more than one word or phrase to describe the same thing. Again, setting coats are no different, and you may also hear setting coats referred to as:

- finish

- skim

- thin coat.

Whichever term you use, and whichever method of application or type of plaster is used, the basic principle remains the same: to achieve a smooth, flat surface that is free from blemishes and defects and is ready to receive the required decorative finish.

Finish plasters are applied at a minimum 2mm and maximum 5mm thickness, depending on the method specified.

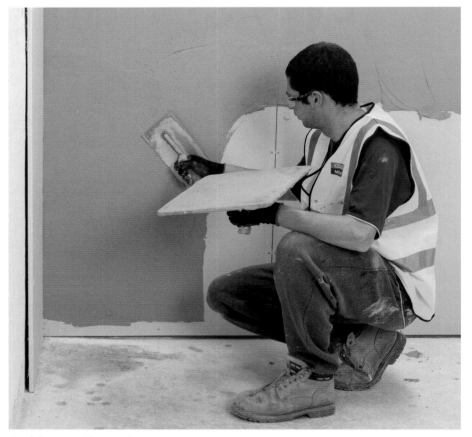

Applying a setting coat

TOOLS AND EQUIPMENT

The tools and equipment used for mixing, applying and finishing setting coats are very much the same as used for render and float coats. However there are a few slight differences, explained in the following table.

Tool	Use
Mixing wheel or electric paddle	For mixing gauges of setting plaster.
Mixing bucket	For mixing gauges of setting plaster in.
Wash bucket	For washing the mixing equipment in.
Cleaning brush	For washing the mixing equipment.
Bucket trowel	For clearing the build-up of dry powder that happens while mixing and for emptying the bucket.

Tool	Use
Spot board and stand 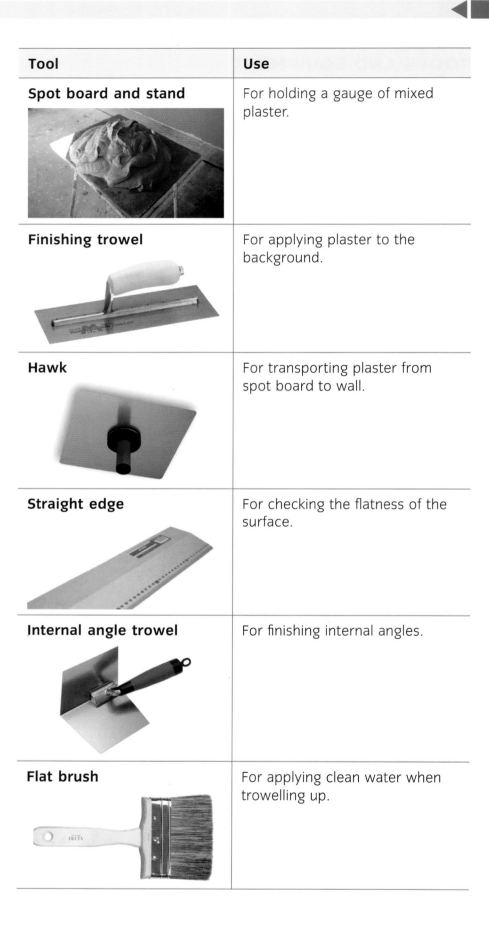	For holding a gauge of mixed plaster.
Finishing trowel	For applying plaster to the background.
Hawk	For transporting plaster from spot board to wall.
Straight edge	For checking the flatness of the surface.
Internal angle trowel	For finishing internal angles.
Flat brush	For applying clean water when trowelling up.

Tool	Use
Spatula	To aid flattening and finishing of the skimming coat.
Hand brush	For cleaning tools while working.
Floor scraper	For cleaning the area while working.
Hop-up	To ease plastering at the top of the wall.

MATERIALS USED FOR SETTING COATS

The vast majority of finish plaster applied in modern construction is gypsum. Before the widespread use of gypsum, plasters were made from lime. Even today, if a lime backing plaster has been used then a lime finish plaster should also be used. It is important to have an understanding of how lime works and its place in more traditional construction. However, it will be covered in greater depth at both Level 2 and Level 3. This chapter is largely concerned with more modern gypsum finishes.

Gypsum finish plasters come as a pre-mixed powder in 25kg bags and only require being added to water and mixed to the correct consistency. They are specially formulated for different backgrounds, applications and durabilities. Below is a table of finish plasters and the backgrounds to which they can be applied.

Type of finish plaster	Use
Multi-purpose setting coat	For use on boards and backing plasters.
Plasterboard finish	For use on low-suction backgrounds, such as plasterboards and Thistle Dri-Coat.
Spray finish	For use on lightweight plaster and plasterboard backgrounds.
Hard grade plaster finish	For use where a stronger finish is required, eg in hallways, corridors, schools and hospitals.

The method of manufacturing gypsum finish plasters is the same as for gypsum backing plasters, producing a class B retarded hemihydrate plaster. They have a very fine aggregate in the form of perlite; quartz is also contained in the plaster.

OUR HOUSE

1 Choose a suitable type of lightweight plaster to be used for setting the walls in 'Our House'. Give reasons for your choice.
2 Work out the amount of plaster that would be required for setting one of the bedrooms.

PLASTER STORAGE AND HANDLING

Bags of gypsum finish plaster have a three-month shelf life, meaning that they must be used within three months of being manufactured. The manufacturers print a use by date on the side of the bags. When taking delivery of or buying the plaster, always check that it is within its use by date. If it is not, or if it is very close to the date, do not accept it but seek advice from your supervisor. When taking any deliveries it is important to check that everything is there and in good condition. If it is not, make a note of it on the delivery note and get the driver to sign it to confirm the discrepancy.

Plaster delivery

Bonded

Overlapping the bags on each layer with those on the layer below

Plaster should be stored under cover and off the floor in a dry and well-ventilated storage area. When stacking bags of plaster, they should be **bonded** – this will make the stack more stable. The stacks should be no more than 1m high. A well-kept store is essential to help minimise damage and waste.

A well-ordered storage area

When handling the bags of plaster, take care not to tear the bags. The dry powder can be an irritant to eyes and skin as well as pose a risk to the respiratory system.

PREPARING BACKGROUNDS FOR SETTING COATS

Before applying setting coats, it is important that the background surface is prepared correctly. For plasterboard backgrounds, this involves:

- checking that there are enough fixings

- checking that the fixings are correctly spaced and at the correct depth

- checking that the boards are staggered

- applying scrim to all joints

- making sure the plasterboards are dust free.

With a floated background, an adequate key should have been provided with a devil float while the floating coat was still soft. This will have dragged up small **nodules** of plaster, leaving a rough surface to the floating coat. These nodules have to be scraped off by lightly running the edge of a trowel over the surface – do not use your best laying-on trowel for this! Also check the surface for suction and straightness.

Nodules

Small balls of plaster left behind on the surface after devil floating. They are created from the plaster dragged out of the grooves by the nails of the devil float when forming the key

Scraping off nodules

Sand/cement floating coats have to be left for between four to seven days before a setting coat can be applied. This allows the material to completely dry and for any shrinkage to take place. Applying the setting coat before the background has fully shrunk will lead to cracking as the background continues to shrink, putting the thin, brittle setting coat under stress.

Because the floating coat has been allowed to dry, the degree of suction it will have will be high. This will need to be controlled by wetting the surface down using a fine mist from a hose or a garden sprayer.

A shrinkage crack

Green

Where plaster has set but not fully hardened

Lightweight backing plasters do not have the same issues with shrinkage. Because of this, the setting coat is best applied while the floating coat is still **green**. That means it has set but not yet fully dried out, so there is still enough water within the floating coat to prevent the suction from being too high. If you were to press a thumb into the plaster you would not leave a dent, but if you were to drag your nail across it you would leave a scratch.

Whether a floating coat is green or dried out can be identified by the change in colour that it undergoes. When a lightweight floating coat has become uniformly darker, it is ready to receive a setting coat. If, however, it has been left to dry out, it will look much lighter and have a high degree of suction. This would need to be controlled by applying a primer or PVA, taking care to follow the manufacturer's instructions.

A lightweight backing plaster at different stages of set

INDUSTRY TIP

As a general guide when using lightweight backing plasters for floating coats, it is best to apply the floating coats in the morning and the setting coats in the afternoon. A cheaper way and the one often used on site is to dampen down the wall with water.

MIXING FINISH PLASTERS

When mixing finish plasters, it is vitally important that all tools and equipment are clean. Because the finish is applied only a few millimetres thick, any hard pieces of old plaster that may have built up on the mixing equipment could break loose and fall into the mix. If this happens, they can drag gouges out of the setting finish plaster as you **trowel up**. This can be very difficult to put right. Dirty tools and equipment can contaminate any fresh plaster that comes into contact with them, causing a **flash set**.

Trowel up

The final procedure in the finishing process when a smooth texture is achieved

Flash set

Where gypsum plaster sets far more quickly than expected. Can be caused by using dirty or contaminated water, tools and equipment, or out-of-date or poorly stored plaster

Dirty mixing equipment

HEALTH AND SAFETY ISSUES

Before you start mixing finish plasters, you need to be aware of the health and safety issues involved with this type of work.

If you are using an electric paddle mixer, make sure it is suitable for the job. It should be 110V and in good working order, and you must have been trained in how to use it.

If a transformer is being used to reduce mains voltage from 230V to 110V, make sure that the transformer is in good working order, too, and that you have been trained to use it. Do not use any extension leads from the mains supply to the transformer – if an extension lead is required, use a yellow 110V lead from the transformer to the mixer. The extension lead must also be in good working order and must not pose a risk, such as by creating a trip hazard.

A well-ordered mixing area

The mixing area should be large enough to work in safely and should be well ventilated. You will also need appropriate PPE, such as:

- a dust mask
- goggles/glasses
- long-sleeved overalls
- gloves
- ear defenders/plugs.

Wearing PPE when mixing setting coats

THE MIXING PROCESS

The following step-by-step guide shows how to mix finish plaster.

STEP 1 Ensure all your equipment is clean and use only clean cold water, of drinking quality.

STEP 2 For a full bucket of plaster, use half a bucket of water. Mixed plaster is twice the volume of water used. Always add the plaster to the water, stirring it in as you add it.

STEP 3 Begin mixing once the water has been soaked up by the dry plaster.

STEP 4 As you add the plaster powder and mix it in, it will become thicker and dry powder will begin to collect around the inside of the bucket. Scrape the bucket clean with a gauging trowel and put the dry powder into the mix.

STEP 5 The mix is ready when a creamy consistency has been achieved and the plaster retains its shape. Scoop a small amount onto a gauging trowel and see if it will drop off. It should just stay in place and only fall off when encouraged to do so with a gentle shake of the trowel.

STEP 6 When the mix is ready, thoroughly clean the mixing equipment.

STEP 7 Dampen down the spot board.

STEP 8 Empty the whole bucket onto the dampened-down spot board, being careful not to transfer any dirt or grit from the floor onto the spot board.

STEP 9 Immediately clean the bucket. This is easiest to do when the plaster is still wet. You will then be ready to make another mix, should you need to.

ACTIVITY

When you're next in the workshop or workplace, follow the steps on the previous page to mix a setting plaster.

INDUSTRY TIP

Do not over mix gypsum plasters as this can dramatically reduce their setting time.

INDUSTRY TIP

A common saying that refers to cleaning plaster from tools and equipment is: 'Easy when wet, hard when set.'

Always put your plaster onto a spot board. This not only makes it easier to use but also keeps the plaster workable for longer. If you leave the plaster in the bucket and load your hawk by scooping out a trowel at a time, not only is this messier but the plaster in the bucket is likely to set more quickly. This is because of the chemical reaction that occurs when plaster powder is mixed with water and starts off the setting process. When this happens heat is produced, known as the heat of hydration. When the plaster is on a spot board it has a larger surface area exposed to the open air, so the heat is allowed to escape. But plaster left in the bucket retains the heat, which speeds up the set of the plaster.

Another reason for transferring your plaster to a spot board is that it allows you to clean your tools and equipment right away. If you left the plaster in the bucket, you would not be able to clean it until all the plaster has been used. This is harder to do with setting plaster and takes longer, and in the meantime the plaster you have already applied is setting.

APPLYING SETTING COATS

To achieve a good finish with setting coats, there are two main factors to consider:

- suction
- timing.

Understanding how these affect the plaster will help you achieve a good finish.

SUCTION

A high-suction background will dry out the plaster too quickly. It will then be more difficult to work with, shrinkage cracks will be likely to occur and the plaster will not achieve its full strength. In order to prevent this, the suction needs to be reduced by either wetting the surface down or applying a primer. See Chapter 3 for more information about preparing backgrounds.

TIMING

As the plaster sets, there are a number of different processes that you need to follow to achieve a good finish. These processes will determine how good the finish will be. Identifying and timing these stages will become easier with experience.

When applying finish plaster, you start at the opposite end of the wall to backing plasters. So a right-handed plasterer, when applying finish plaster, would start at the top left-hand corner. This is to minimise the lines left behind by the trowel. As the plaster is laid on, the toe of the trowel overlaps the plaster that has already been laid on. Because of the way a trowel wears, its corners become more rounded at the toe than at the heel, leaving fewer lines behind. Ideally, a trowel that has been **broken in** should be used for applying and finishing setting coats.

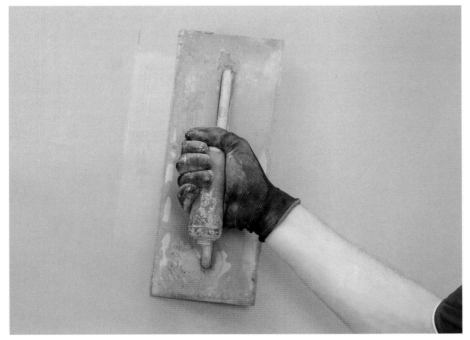

A broken in trowel

Broken in

Describing a well-used trowel, which has a more flexible blade, the corners have been rounded off and the edge is sharper. This makes applying finishing coats easier

ACTIVITY

Look at some online tool catalogues and find out how much a finishing trowel can cost. How much variation is there between prices?

INDUSTRY TIP

Professional plasterers have at least three plastering trowels:

- one that is broken in and only used for setting
- a second that is partially broken in and is used for applying backing plasters
- a third, new trowel.

If anything should happen to your best setting trowel then the partially broken in one can replace it.

INDUSTRY TIP

Trowels can be bought pre-worn or can be worn in through use.

APPLICATION

The setting coat is considered as one coat of plaster but actually consists of two applications of finish plaster. The first application is laid on, using a trowel, so it completely covers the background surface to a depth of 1mm. Once this first coat has become tacky, the second application is laid on, also using a trowel, completely covering the first and bringing the total thickness of the plaster to 2mm. This is known as the 'trowel trowel' method. After this it is finished in the way outlined later in this section.

The following step-by-step guide describes how to apply and finish a setting coat to a floated background and to plasterboards, using the trowel trowel method.

STEP 1 Ensure the background is prepared. For plasterboards, this involves checking fixings and applying scrim. For floated backgrounds, this involves scraping off any loose aggregate and controlling suction.

STEP 2 Start at the top of the wall. Working across from the left to the right, apply the plaster on flat and evenly. Work two trowel widths across to the other side of the wall, returning the trowel from the right-hand corner once the top of the wall has been completed.

STEP 3 Lay on the first full trowel. Starting from around waist height with an open and full trowel, spread the plaster up the wall to a thickness of approximate 2mm. Ensure that the toe of the trowel overlaps the previously applied layer. Turn the trowel's face into the wall as you go so that when you reach the band at the ceiling line the face of the trowel is virtually flat to the wall.

STEP 4 Using a downward stroke and a closed trowel face, flatten down the plaster that has just been laid on.

STEP 5 Take off any excess and flatten the surface using an upward stroke. With a slightly more open trowel, take off any excess and fill any misses where the plaster has not completely covered the background.

STEP 6 Repeat Steps 3–5 to complete the wall, working from the left to the right. As you get to the right side of the wall, return the plaster into the previously laid surface.

STEP 7 Do not go right to the floor but stop approximately 25mm above it. This will not only stop you from accidentally picking up bits of grit onto your trowel from the floor but will also reduce the risk of the bottom edge of the plaster **kicking out**. The whole surface is then flattened off.

STEP 8 The second application. Once the first application has pulled in, make a fresh mix of plaster and lay on the second application in the same way, repeating Steps 2–7. Do not try to smooth out any lines left by the trowel in the first application.

INDUSTRY TIP

As you get better at applying setting coats you may be able to start from the floor and work upwards to the top layer.

Kicking out

Where plaster forms a thicker ridge along the bottom of a wall. This makes it difficult for skirting boards to be fitted as they cannot sit flush to the wall

ACTIVITY

To help achieve a good finish to your setting coat, practise applying setting coats to a sheet of plasterboard using the steps on this page.

LAYING DOWN

Once the two applications of finish plaster have been applied to the background, you must leave it to pick up slightly before continuing with the next process. The temptation is to try and smooth out all the lines. Do not try this as the plaster will be too wet: all that you will manage to do is move the plaster around without smoothing out the lines. How long the plaster should be left to pick up before the next process – known as 'laying down' – is carried out will depend on many variables. These are:

- how much suction the background has

- how thick the mix was

- how near the plaster was to its use by date

- how well the plaster had been stored

- how big an area has been laid on

- how thickly the plaster has been applied

- the room temperature.

These factors will all have an influence on how quickly the plaster sets. However, approximately 5–10 minutes is a good guide.

While waiting for the plaster to pick up, it is a good idea to clean down your spot board. Put a trowel full of the remaining plaster to one side for use later on and discard the rest, in accordance with current legislation. Clean your tools and change the water in your water bucket. Also, clean up your work area but be careful not to damage the freshly applied plaster or get dust and grit onto it when sweeping up.

While you are cleaning up, it is important to keep an eye on how the plaster is picking up. When the plaster has picked up sufficiently, the next stage is to flatten out all the trowel lines left behind during the laying on process. This is done by holding the blade of the trowel at an angle of around 15° to the surface being laid in and applying sufficient pressure to flatten the plaster. Too shallow an angle will result in the drag marks being smeared across the surface, while too steep an angle will scrape off the plaster.

Any misses in the plaster's coverage, known as **gauls**, can also be filled at this point using a firmer pressure and the plaster put to one side. Because the plaster that has been laid on and the plaster used to fill gauls are from the same mix, they are the same consistency and therefore they blend together easily, filling the gauls.

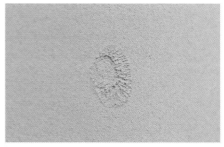

Indentation left after testing whether plaster has picked up – the plaster is now ready

Misses and gauls in plaster

Gaul

A hollow or miss on the surface of the finished plaster

The following steps show how to flatten out the setting coat.

STEP 1 Cut off the excess. Using the toe of your trowel, run along the internal angles. The corner of your trowel should be scraping the adjacent surface, separating any plaster that has got onto it from the wall.

STEP 2 Using the toe of your trowel, scrape off any plaster from the adjacent surfaces.

STEP 3 Lay down the internals. Using a clean, wet trowel, flatten the plaster along the internal angles. Fill any gauls and hollows with the fresh plaster that you put aside earlier. This should give you nice neat internal angles.

STEP 4 Using a clean wet trowel and working toe to heel, lay down by drawing the trowel down the wall from the ceiling line to just above waist height. Apply enough pressure to flatten out all the lines. Fill gauls and hollows with the fresh plaster.

INDUSTRY TIP

Keep the trowel wet so that it doesn't stick to the wall.

STEP 5 Continue repeating Step 4 until you reach the end of the wall. Lay down the bottom of the wall, repeating Steps 4–5 but, instead of coming down the wall, start at the base and trowel up the wall to meet the previous work.

TROWELLING UP

The wall should now be flat, with all trowel lines smoothed out and any misses and hollows filled. However, the wall is still not finished. If it was left to dry at this stage it would feel rough to the touch and be very porous.

So the next stage in the finishing process is what is known as 'wet trowelling' or 'trowelling up'. This involves brushing a small amount of clean water onto the plastered surface, then, with the trowel, removing the water. This will close in the surface of the plaster, making it smoother to the touch.

To do this, you will need a clean bucket of water, a 150mm flat brush (a paint brush), a 25mm water brush and the remains of the plaster that you put to one side for the laying-down process.

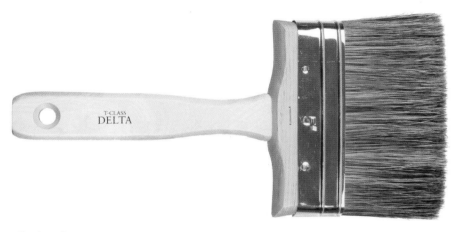

A flat brush

The plaster will by now have stiffened up considerably and should have the firmness of cheddar. When wet trowelling, it is important to remove all the water applied to the surface without scraping off the plaster. As with the laying-down process, hold the blade of the trowel at an angle of around 15° to the surface being trowelled and apply sufficient pressure. Too shallow an angle will result in the water being smeared across the surface, while too steep an angle will scrape the plaster's surface and, instead of closing the pores, will actually open them up. Avoid using too much water as this will weaken the set.

The following steps show trowelling up.

STEP 1 Using a brush and clean water, brush in the internal angles.

STEP 2 Begin trowelling up. Use a long bristle brush dipped in clean water. From the corner in which you started, brush or splash a small amount of water onto the plastered surface, about 300mm down. Immediately follow this with the trowel to around or just above waist height, removing the water. Start at the top, working across from left to right.

STEP 3 Continue wet trowelling in this way until you reach the other end of the wall. Any residue left on the trowel (known as **fat**) must be cleaned off before the next stroke.

STEP 4 Trowel up the bottom of the wall. Brush a small amount of clean water onto the wall and trowel up as before, using only an upward motion.

Fat

The residue on a trowel created from trowelling up. This is dead plaster that should be discarded. If used to fill holes and misses it will not set properly – it will shrink and become soft and dusty

INDUSTRY TIP

If you angle your trowel so that the toe is slightly in front of the heel but keeping the face of the blade at approximately 15°, the water will run off the back, keeping the wall clean and indicating where you have been.

Hard trowelling

The final trowel can be done just after the wet trowelling. It is carried out with a firm trowel; this is called 'hard trowelling'. This is done to give the plaster a smooth, matt texture. Care should be taken not to over trowel the plaster because this will polish the surface (make the finished plaster gurnished). This is undesirable as it will be difficult to decorate and require sanding down to provide a key for the paint.

DEVELOPMENTS AND INNOVATIONS

Although some aspects of plastering have not changed much over the centuries, there are always new products coming onto the market. Some are introduced in response to changing legislation, while others are the result of improved manufacturing techniques.

Speedskim® plasterer's rule

ACTIVITY

Use an internet search engine to look up new products from companies such as British Gypsum, Knauf, Lafarge and Speedskim®. Write a brief summary of what the products are used for.

ACTIVITY

Using the internet, find out about Joseph Aspdin.

Spatulas are being used more often these days, to flatten in the first and second coats of skim, as is the new Speedskim® rule (see photo above). Using these tools is proving popular with lots of companies. They make life a lot easier for plasterers as they give coverage of a larger area and improve the quality of finish.

Spray finish plasters are also now available on the market. This method allows for large areas to be covered, which is more cost effective. Some companies have tried to manufacture a universal plaster plus PVA but this is proving difficult because of the properties of the material.

Case Study: Matthew

Matthew is a young trainee plasterer who has been given a job of setting a new plasterboard wall which is 3.5m long and 2.2m high. Although Matthew has worked with experienced plasterers before, this is his first setting job on his own.

Matthew has worked out how much finish plaster he requires using calculations and reading the manufacturer's instructions on coverage. He checked the plasterboard for straightness and plumb, and applied the tape. He then mixed the finish plaster. He applied the first coat starting at the top of the wall and working across, and then worked his way down the wall.

Matthew mixed the second coat and started the laying-down process. He then left the wall for a few minutes to pull in and firm up. Matthew then took the lines out. The next stage was to add a little water and trowel up. When the wall was finished, he cleaned up and went home.

The next day Matthew came into work to find his boss and the site agent looking at his wall. The wall had lots of misses and gauls. Also, in places, too much water had been used and this had caused the surface to become weak. The boss told Matthew, 'You added too much water and did not pay attention with the laying-down coat.' It was at this point that Matthew realised his mistake. So he applied PVA to the surface to kill the suction and re-plastered the wall. Matthew had learnt a valuable lesson: always follow the steps for applying the setting coat.

Work through the following questions to check your learning.

1 What class of plaster is gypsum finish plaster?

   a A hemihydrate.

   b A retarded hemihydrate.

   c B hemihydrate.

   d B retarded hemihydrate.

2 Which of the following types of sand is used in lime finish plaster?

   a Coarse.

   b Red.

   c Silver.

   d Soft.

3 The water used for mixing finish plaster should be

   a cold and clean

   b cold and dirty

   c hot and dirty

   d hot and clean.

4 When finish plaster is mixed, by how much has the volume increased in relation to the amount of water used?

   a It does not increase.

   b Two times.

   c Three times.

   d Four times.

5 How many applications are required when using setting plaster?

   a 1.

   b 2.

   c 3.

   d 4.

6 What voltage should an electric whisk be?

   a 24V.

   b 110V.

   c 230V.

   d 400V.

7 What is the term given to the dead plaster trowelled off the wall?

   a Fat.

   b Grease.

   c Lard.

   d Oil.

8 What is the term for a miss in the finished plasterwork?

   a Gaul.

   b Ghoul.

   c Growl.

   d Grail.

9 Which one of the following backgrounds is suitable for a setting coat?

   a Brickwork.

   b Render coat.

   c Blockwork.

   d Floating coat.

10 What date is found on bags of plaster?

   a Best before.

   b Sell by.

   c Manufactured on.

   d Use by.

11 How many 25kg bags of plaster are in a 1,000kg delivery?

a 40.

b 60.

c 100.

d 250.

12 Cold clean water is used for mixing plaster to prevent

a first set

b flash set

c second set

d slow set.

13 What is over-trowelled finished plaster said to be?

a Polished.

b Grainished.

c Gurnished.

d Tarnished.

14 What is the consequence of over-trowelled plaster?

a It will not adhere correctly.

b It will be difficult to remove.

c It will not be straight.

d It will be difficult to decorate.

15 Over mixing plaster will cause it to set

a harder

b quicker

c more slowly

d stronger.

16 Which one of the following tools is used to key the floating coat?

a Chamfered float.

b Demon float.

c Devil float.

d Skimming float.

17 Which one of the following is a recommended thickness for a setting coat when applied to a backing plaster?

a 1mm.

b 10mm.

c 2mm.

d 20mm.

18 Where should a right-handed plasterer begin applying the setting coat to a wall?

a Bottom left.

b Bottom right.

c Top left.

d Top right.

19 What is the equipment onto which a mix of plaster is emptied ready for use?

a Hawk and stand.

b Spot board and stand.

c Board and trestle.

d Spot board and trestle.

20 Which one of the following is the correct tool to use when applying setting plaster?

a Gauging trowel.

b Bucket trowel.

c Finishing trowel.

d Angle trowel.

Chapter 8
Introduction to floor screeding

Past this point
Thank You

Although screeding is a subject that will be covered in greater detail at Level 2, this chapter will give you an introduction into the materials used and the processes employed. This will give you knowledge that you can build on in order to successfully complete the screeding unit at Level 2, with a full understanding of the subject.

By reading this chapter you will know about:

1 What screeding is.
2 Health and safety requirements.
3 Tools and equipment used.
4 Types of screed.
5 Materials and mixes used.
6 Techniques used for laying screeds.
7 Curing.

WHAT IS A FLOOR SCREED?

A floor screed is a top layer of material (traditionally a mix of sand and cement) that is poured on top of the building's floor **substrate** to create a level floor. Screeds can be laid in a range of different thicknesses, to bring the surface of the floor to the height specified in the architect's plans. They also provide an appropriate surface for a specified flooring, such as vinyl, carpet or wooden flooring, although these days sometimes screed is left bare in order to create an 'industrial' feel to a building.

Laying floor screed

Substrate

A stable background onto which other materials can be applied

Screeding is traditionally thought of as the role of the plasterer. Indeed, there are many who think you cannot truly call yourself a plasterer unless you have comprehensive knowledge of all the different aspects of the craft, including floor screeds. However, with the modern development of more and more different specialist floor coverings, screeding is increasingly being considered as a trade in its own right and as something that operatives specialise in. However, many of the skills and techniques used in solid plastering are also used in screeding.

INDUSTRY TIP

Mixing is a very important part of floor screeding. When laying a traditional sand and cement floor screed, a mix ratio of 3:1 should be used. This should be mixed to a semi-dry state. This means that, when the mix is squeezed in the hand, it stays together. If the mix falls apart or cracks in the hand, then it is too dry.

HEALTH AND SAFETY ISSUES

There are health and safety issues that need to be taken into account when screeds are being mixed and laid. For example, the dust created by the cement when it is being added to the mix can cause respiratory illness. Measures need to be taken to either reduce the levels of dust and/or to reduce your exposure to the dust. These measures can include ensuring that mixing takes place in a well-ventilated area, and that fine-particle dust masks or respirators are worn when mixing. Gloves and eye goggles should also be worn, as well as the standard hi-viz clothing and safety boots.

Wearing correct PPE for mixing

When the mix is being laid, it no longer poses a significant risk from fine dust particles. However, the cement is an irritant and can cause severe chemical burns. This is made worse by the abrasive action of the sand and by the fact that you may well be kneeling in it as you work. To prevent this from being a problem, a long-sleeved, heavy-duty pair of moisture-resistant overalls and a good pair of knee pads should be worn.

Wearing PPE when screeding floors

By its very nature, laying floor screeds requires you to be working while kneeling, bending over and stretching. This can put a lot of strain on the back, so working for long periods without a break should be avoided. More on health and safety can found in Chapter 1. It is also covered at Level 2.

TOOLS AND EQUIPMENT

The tools and equipment used for screeding differ slightly from those used in solid plastering. They include those listed below.

Tools	Use
Floor laying trowel	For trowelling the floor screed smooth.
Float	Used to compact the screed, as well as to provide a finish.
Box rule	For ruling in screeds and checking the level.

Tools	Use
Spirit level	Used to ensure a level surface.
Water level	For setting a datum line.
Square	For setting the screeds at the datum level.
Mixer	For mixing materials.
Screed rail	To help keep the floor flat.

TYPES OF SCREED

Before you begin to lay a screed, you must first establish where the screed is to go. Consulting relevant architect's drawings, such as the location drawings and assembly drawings, will give you this information. However, you must also read the specification that goes with the drawing. The specification, or 'spec.', will detail the type of screed, its mix ratios, the desired thickness and any preparation required, among other information. (More about specifications and drawings can be found in Chapter 2.)

There are three main types of sand and cement screed. These are:

- monolithic
- bonded
- unbonded.

MONOLITHIC

When something is described as being monolithic, it means it is made up of a single, unbroken mass. When a monolithic floor screed is laid, it is laid within three hours of the concrete slab substrate having been poured. The concrete has by then undergone its initial set but has yet to go through its final set. This means that as the screed, which has been laid on top, begins to set, it chemically bonds with the concrete as they both set and dry.

Because of the construction method of monolithic floors, the substrate (concrete slab) and screed topping dry as one mass. This results in a more reliable and trouble-free floor, less likely to blow or de-bond. However, this type of screed must be laid on freshly poured concrete within the specified time period. If the concrete dries out before the screed is laid, they will not bond or dry as one mass.

The screed is laid to a thickness of 12–25mm. This type of screed is often found in commercial settings such as factories and warehouses.

BONDED

As the name suggests, this type of floor screed is bonded to the substrate. The substrate is allowed to completely dry out and set before the screed is laid. Pre-formed concrete slabs and concrete block floors are also suitable substrates for this type of screed.

The method of bonding the screed to the substrate is by using a cement and PVA grout as a bonding agent. The floor is prepared by **scabbling** the surface of the concrete. This not only removes the **laitance** but also roughens up the surface, providing a good key.

Screed 12–25mm

Concrete sub-base

Monolithic screed

Scabbling

The removal of the surface finish by mechanical means, producing a suitable key

Laitance

A layer of weak material that comes to the top of concrete as it sets

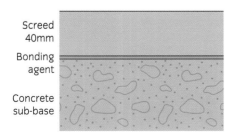

Screed 40mm

Bonding agent

Concrete sub-base

Bonded floor screed

Scabbling should only be carried out by trained operatives wearing all the correct PPE. The substrate is then swept clean of any dust and dirt before being soaked overnight with clean water to kill any suction. While the floor is still damp but with no standing water left on its surface, a slurry of neat cement PVA and water is applied not less than 20 minutes before laying the screed.

The screed in this type of screeding should be at least 40mm thick.

Concrete scabbling

UNBONDED

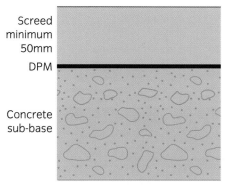

Screed minimum 50mm
DPM
Concrete sub-base

Unbonded floor screed with DPM

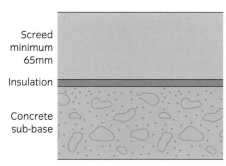

Screed minimum 65mm
Insulation
Concrete sub-base

Floating floor screed

Unbonded floors come in two types. The first type has a damp proof membrane (DPM) between the concrete substrate and the screed. The only preparation required is that the substrate is swept clean of any debris that might puncture the DPM. The DPM is then laid in position and lapped up the walls and at joins by 100mm.

However, it is becoming more and more common for unbonded screeds to be constructed in the second type, using the floating floor method. This method is where the substrate, as well as having the DPM laid on top, then has a layer of insulation on top of that. This not only makes it easier to conform to current legislation regarding energy efficiency, it also allows for underfloor heating to be installed, because having insulation means that the underfloor heating only heats up the screed, not the substrate, the ground or the building's structure.

Unbonded screeds are laid to a minimum thickness of 50mm, but can be 65mm thick for floating screeds with underfloor heating.

Lapped DPM

ACTIVITY

Draw a cross-section of a monolithic floor, a bonded floor and an unbonded floor on DPM. Use the correct symbols for each material found in the floors' construction.

Floating floor with underfloor heating

MATERIALS AND MIXES USED IN SCREEDING

Whichever type of screed you lay, the materials are basically the same. The aggregate is made up of well-graded sharp coarse sand, with particles ranging from 9mm down to fines. The binder is Ordinary Portland Cement (OPC) mixed at the ratio of 3:1 sand to cement. Additives may include the following.

- *Retarders*: Used to slow the set of the screed, allowing time to lay large areas without joins in one go

- *Waterproofers*: These may be added if the screeds are to be laid in wet areas

- *Reinforcement*: As a way of reducing the risk of shrinkage cracks occurring, strands of chopped polypropylene fibre (PPF) can be introduced into the mix.

From left to right: retarders, waterproofer and reinforcement

The best and most accurate way of ensuring that the screed is mixed in the correct proportions and to the right consistency is to have it delivered pre-mixed, although there is usually a minimum volume order for deliveries so this may not be possible for small jobs. If pre-mixed delivery is not an option, then on-site mixing will be necessary.

MIXING ON SITE

When mixing on site, it is essential to accurately gauge the proportions of the mix materials, using a gauge box or buckets. This ensures that the strength is correct and consistent for subsequent mixes.

Mixing on site should result in a good, even distribution of the materials throughout the mix. The materials should first be dry mixed thoroughly, before adding water, then mixing some more to evenly distribute the water throughout the mix. Take care not to add too much water.

The mix should be semi-dry, meaning that it is moist but not wet. If a small handful is squeezed, it should clump together but not leave your hand wet, and when dropped it should only just break open, not scatter.

Forming the mix into a clump to test for wetness

Clumped mix that has not fallen apart after clumping

On-site mixing can be done in a number of ways.

■ *Hand mixing*: This requires the materials to be mixed together using a shovel. The materials are piled at one end of the area to be screeded. Using the shovel, move the pile to the other end and back again, twice, adding a little more water each time as required until mixed. This is time consuming and arduous work which can result in inconsistent mixes.

Mixing by hand

■ *Drum mixing*: This is where the materials are mixed in a cement mixer and tumbled until mixed. Ensure that there are no unmixed materials stuck at the back of the mixer. Care needs to be taken when adding water as the tumbling action of the materials being mixed together can cause balls of compacted materials to form.

A drum mixer

ACTIVITY

Calculate the volume of sand required for a floor screed to be laid in a room measuring 3m × 2.5m. The screed has an average thickness of 65mm.

■ *Pan mixer*: This is probably the best way of mixing screeding materials on site. The pan mixer has a large pan with two steel wheels that rotate around a central column in the pan. The materials are placed in the pan and the rotary action of the wheel forces the materials together. When the mix is ready, a gate in the base of the pan is opened and the mix is pushed through the gate.

A pan mixer

TECHNIQUES USED FOR LAYING SCREEDS

To achieve a level surface, you must first set out some dots to the correct depth or thickness. The levels for these can be taken from a datum. (See Chapter 1, page 47 for more about datum points.) Next, set battens between the dots, forming small screeds from which the rest of the floor can be ruled. This way you can divide the floor area up into bays, rather like the way that walls are set out for floating coats. Make sure that the box rule is 300mm longer than the distance between the screeds.

On new builds, you will often find a datum line drawn around the perimeter of the room indicated as 1m above finished floor level (1m FFL). This means that if the screed you are laying is the finished floor then it needs to finish 1m or 1,000mm below this line. If, however, the screed will be topped by an 8mm-thick floor tile bedded onto 2mm-thick adhesive as the floor's finish, then your floor screed will need to finish 1.01m or 1,010mm below this line. This allows room for the 10mm combined thickness of the tile and adhesive.

The following steps show you how to lay the floor to the datum line using a tape measure.

STEP 1 Damp down the floor.

STEP 2 Sweep the floor.

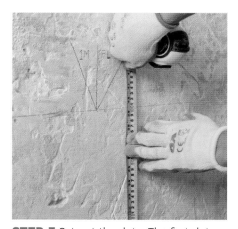

STEP 3 Set out the dots. The first dot should be set in the corner furthest from the door and approximately 300mm from the end of the wall forming the room's longest length. Use a tape measure to make sure the dot is the required distance below the datum.

STEP 4 Set further dots as required. Ensure each dot is the same distance below the datum line. Level the dots across.

STEP 5 Form screeds between the dots. Ensure they are in line and flush with the top of the dots and are level along their length.

STEP 6 Rule in floor to dots with a box rule.

STEP 7 Before you lay beyond what you can comfortably reach without overstretching, remove the dots, fill their holes and float the surface of the floor, filling any misses and hollows, etc. Check the floor with a box rule.

STEP 8 Repeat Steps 5–7 along the opposite wall to form another screed.

STEP 9 You should now have two screeds ruled in to dots and levelled in from the datum.

STEP 10 Fill in between the screeds. Starting at the back wall of the room, empty a wheelbarrow of mix between the screeds. This will need to be compacted down as firmly as is possible, then ruled off flush with the screeds.

STEP 11 Follow the same process for the back screed, applying screed and compacting the mix.

STEP 12 Rule in the screed with a box rule and float.

STEP 13 Use a trowel to smooth the screeds.

STEP 14 Continue in this manner, compacting, ruling and floating, working methodically towards the door.

STEP 15 Complete the floor with a trowel.

STEP 16 Carry out a final check for level.

An arguably more accurate way to set out floor screeds is to re-position the datum to a more convenient height. This is done by measuring down at each corner of the room to the required distance from the existing datum. Using a chalk line, join these points up to form a new workable datum.

Chalk line

LAYING SCREED TO A DATUM LINE USING A SQUARE

From the set finished floor level datum, measure down and set your own datum at a level suitable for the square to be used. Set the dots to the required level and mark on the square the point where the datum intersects. Ensure that the mark on the square lines up with the datum line for each dot.

Using the same mix as for the floor screed, bed battens between the dots. Ensure that they are in line and flush with the top of the dots and level along their length.

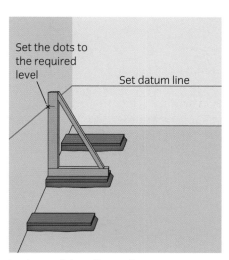

Laying a datum line using a square

Using battens

◀

If a datum line is not available, your levels can be taken from the bottom of a door liner, the bottom of a staircase or, in some cases, from an existing floor level. If you do this, set your first dot in a convenient place and transfer the levels.

Laying a floor screed to a fall, ie a sloping floor, requires the same preparation and sequence of operations as for a level floor except for setting out the dots. When laying to falls, dots and rails are laid to allow liquid to drain in a given direction. After the datum line has been set out, the fall or slope is then marked from the datum line on the wall accordingly. Generally, the work should start from the lowest point, taking into consideration any bumps or unevenness in the substrate. This type of floor is required in places such as showers and kennels.

Using battens in screeding

CURING

Curing means keeping the cement moist to allow the screed to fully harden. This is different from drying.

During mixing we use only enough water to allow for ruling and finishing the screed – there is not enough water to complete the 'hydration' of the cement. This means that there is not enough water to allow the cement to harden completely.

You must try to prevent the loss of water from the screed for about seven days by covering it with polythene sheeting or wet sackings, or by the careful use of a hose. This is to keep the water within the floor screed. After seven days, allow the screed to dry 'normally'. The use of curing compounds is not recommended because it can keep water contained in the screed and so affect any further floor coverings.

A screed covered with polythene sheeting

Once the curing has been completed, the floor should be protected against possible damage during the rest of the building operation.

DRYING OUT PERIODS

With sand and cement screeds, one day should be allowed for each millimetre of thickness for the first 50mm, followed by an increasing time for each millimetre beyond that thickness. It is therefore reasonable to expect a levelling screed that is 50mm thick, drying under good conditions, to be sufficiently dry in about two months. All floors should be allowed to dry naturally.

ACTIVITY

Look at older textbooks to see how methods of floor screeding have changed. Look online to find out about pump screeds.

Case Study: Cameron

Cameron is a trainee plasterer who was given a job of laying an unbonded floor screed. The floor area was 3m × 3.2m. His instruction was to lay the floor screed 50mm thick.

Cameron had worked on site with a range of different plasterers and had laid monolithic floor screeds before. He knew that with monolithic floor screeds you have to lay the screeding mix within three hours of the concrete sub-base going down. However, an unbonded floor presented different challenges.

First of all, Cameron calculated the amount of screeding material that he would need. He then prepared the surface by sweeping clean the floor. He then laid down the damp proof membrane with the help of a labourer, making sure that the DPM lapped up the sides of the wall. For this job, Cameron decided to use screed rails as he thought this would help. However, Cameron decided to use pieces of wood that he found lying around on site as screed rails. He made sure he had all the correct PPE, including knee pads and gloves.

First Cameron applied the sand and cement screed material with a shovel. This was then ruled in with a box rule, ruling off the screed rails, and compacted with a float. This process was continued until the floor was completed.

Cameron did a final check with a spirit level. It was only then that he discovered that the floor was neither flat nor level. The foreman was called and he noticed the problem: the wood used was of two different thicknesses. Fortunately the problem was resolved. Two new metal straight screed rails were put in place and ruled off.

Cameron had learned a lesson: if using screed rails for floor screeding, make sure they are perfectly straight and the correct thickness.

Work through the following questions to check your learning.

1   What ratio of sand to cement is used for floor screeds?

    a 3:1.

    b 3:2.

    c 5:1.

    d 6:1.

2   What does FFL stand for?

    a Final floor level.

    b Finished floor level.

    c Flattened floor level.

    d Floor finishing latex.

3   Concrete is keyed by

    a scabbling

    b scrabbling

    c scribing

    d scrubbing.

4   What sand is used for floor screeds?

    a Coarse sharp.

    b Soft.

    c Fine sharp.

    d Silver.

5   What is the cement residue that rises to the top of wet concrete?

    a Latex.

    b Fat.

    c Scum.

    d Laitance.

6   What is used to bond a floor screed to a concrete substrate?

    a Spatterdash.

    b Neat sand.

    c PVA and cement.

    d Any bonding agent.

7   When laying a monolithic floor, what is the **maximum** time between the concrete being laid and the screed being laid?

    a Two hours.

    b Three hours.

    c Four hours.

    d Five hours.

8   Why might retarder be added to a sand and cement screed mix?

    a To strengthen the set.

    b To speed up the set.

    c To slow down the set.

    d To cure the set.

9   What is a datum?

    a A set point from which to take levels.

    b A screed laid to a fall.

    c The batten set in the screed for ruling off.

    d The first screed formed.

10   The DPM is directly beneath what type of screed?

    a Monolithic.

    b Bonded.

    c Unbonded.

    d Floating.

11   The level of a finished floor should be taken from the

    a datum line

    b top of a door lining

    c bottom of a window

    d bottom of stairs.

12 What type of cement is used for floor screeds?

a Rapid hardening.

b Sulphide resisting.

c Ordinary Portland.

d Extra special.

13 What **must** be done prior to laying a bonded screed?

a Thoroughly soak, sweep clean and apply grout.

b Sweep clean, apply grout and thoroughly soak.

c Lightly dampen, sweep clean and apply grout.

d Apply grout, lightly soak and sweep clean.

14 What is the type of floor screed laid on top of insulation boards?

a Bonded.

b Monolithic.

c Floating.

d Separate.

15 Why are some screeds laid to a fall?

a To use less materials.

b To allow for drainage.

c To aid rapid hardening.

d To prevent shrinkage cracks.

16 What should the consistency of the screeding mix be?

a Semi-wet.

b Dry.

c Semi-dry.

d Wet.

17 Compacting the screed will make it

a smooth

b level

c dense

d weak.

18 Which type of floor requires grout to be applied?

a Monolithic.

b Floating.

c Semi-floating.

d Bonded.

19 What is the reason for curing a floor screed?

a To allow for a good finished floor.

b To allow cement to fully harden.

c To keep the floor dry.

d To prevent people walking on the floor.

20 What is the **best** method of curing a floor?

a Cover with a polythene sheet.

b Cover with damp paper.

c Cover with scaffold boards.

d Cover with hard board.

Chapter 9
Introduction to fibrous plastering

Fibrous plastering is a form of pre-cast plasterwork that is ornamental and decorative, creating an elegant appearance. It takes the form of geometric and symmetric designs that reflect styles from different periods of history.

This chapter will help you understand the basic principles involved with fibrous plastering work and will form a foundation for progression to Level 2. You will learn about different techniques and methods of producing mouldwork that have been used by plasterers over generations. This will help develop your knowledge and understanding of the way our heritage has developed and changed over time.

By reading this chapter you will know about:

1 What fibrous plasterworking is.

2 The tools and equipment used.

3 Health and safety issues.

4 Types of reverse moulds.

5 The materials used for producing mouldings.

6 Casting.

7 Positive moulds.

8 Fixing casts.

9 Calculating quantities.

WHAT IS FIBROUS PLASTERING?

Fibrous plastering is a form of moulding work that dates back to the 18th century, when it was made popular by a number of different architects. It has now been part of our heritage for many years and is still popular today.

The majority of plaster castings are premade in fibrous workshops before being fixed on site by plasterers who have specialised in fibrous plastering. Modern fibrous casts are made to be lightweight and strong, in contrast to old-style heavy mouldings that were run in situ and often became problematic over time.

It is a type of **pre-cast** plasterwork that contains either plain features or highly detailed patterns in its design – or a combination of both! Fibrous plasterwork is carried out by specialist craftsmen and women known as fibrous plasterers or 'fibre hands'.

Pre-cast

Moulds that have been cast in a workshop before fixing

Different types of cast mouldings

ACTIVITY

Search the web to find out about Robert Adam, a famous architect who designed different mouldwork.

Reverse mould

A mould that is the 'back to front' version of the shape or pattern that you want to produce

Fibrous plasterwork is produced by mixing fine casting plaster and water, then applying the mixed material over or into **reverse moulds**. This process is known as 'casting'.

The process for making moulds will be explained in detail in the Level 2 textbook, but this chapter gives a good introduction.

Undercut

A model or mould with overhang patterns. They can be difficult to remove when cast unless the reverse mould is made from flexible material

- Plain mouldings with no **undercut** sections can be cast from fibreglass or plaster reverse moulds.

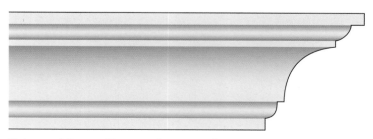

Plain mouldings with no undercut sections

THE CITY & GUILDS TEXTBOOK

- Complex detailed patterns with undercut sections are produced from rubber moulds.

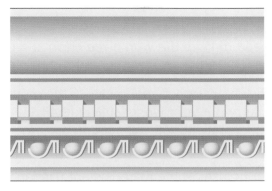

Complex, detailed patterns with undercut sections

- An alternative way of producing a mould without casting from a reverse mould is to run a positive mould on pre-made benches, using a running mould that has a profile to the desired shape.

A positive mould on pre-made benches

Fibrous mouldings are mainly manufactured in workshops known as fibrous shops. These workshops require clean running water for mixing and producing plastering components, an efficient waste disposal area, and a drying store to cure and dry the plaster products.

HEALTH AND SAFETY ISSUES

Before you start to produce any mouldwork, you need to be aware of the health and safety issues involved with this type of work.

- You need to wear appropriate clothing, protecting you from plaster splashes and dust, chemicals, varnishes, hardeners, glues, toxic resins, etc.

- As with any other plastering work, you need to wear appropriate safety clothing such as safety shoes, overalls, dust masks, safety glasses and latex gloves, all of which protect you while allowing you to carry out your work safely.

A dust mask

Gloves

ACTIVITY

Make a list of the flammable materials that you may use when producing moulding work.

Store flammable materials safely

Making good

Repairing or finishing detailed plasterwork using fibrous tools

- On some occasions you will be working with strong glues and hardeners, melting rubber or mixing substances that will require specialist safety equipment such as respirators or heatproof gloves.

- The process of producing moulds can cause build-up of waste and clutter. You need to keep the workplace clean and dispose of waste efficiently before it creates trip and slip hazards.

- Reading the risk assessment and following the method statement will help you carry out your work safely, identifying what safety measures and equipment you will need to use when carrying out specific tasks.

- Fibrous plastering uses some materials not used in other types of plastering. It is important to read the data sheets and COSHH assessments for these materials. These will explain how to use the products in line with the manufacturers' guidelines, and identify any specific hazards and risks when using hazardous substances.

- Flammable materials like varnish and glues will need to be kept under lock and key in steel cabinets.

TOOLS AND EQUIPMENT

Fibrous plastering is considered to be a craft due to the high level of skill involved in producing and fixing this type of detailed moulding work. Unlike solid plastering, this type of work involves fine, detailed tools. The tools and equipment used by fibrous plasterers consist of various small tools as shown in the table below.

Tool	Use
Small tool leaf and square	Used for minor moulding detail work. Also used for filling in joints in fibrous work.
Busk	Small rectangular tool used for **making good** fine jointing and minor defects. These can be different shapes, used depending on the shape and detail of the mould.

Tool	Use
Joint rule 	The joint rule has various uses in moulding work. Joint rules are flat blades and can be used for forming mitre joints. Another use is to form and align fibrous casts during fixing. Old joint rules can be used to scrape clean benches during and after the casting process, removing plaster droppings and splashes.
Small brushes 	Used to clean detail work and sometimes used to apply wet plaster into the recess and joins of moulds where a small tool does not reach.
Casting brush 	The casting brush, also known as a splash brush, has open bristles that are good for retrieving and applying casting plaster onto reverse moulds. The brushes in the photos are the typical types you will use.
Flat workbenches 	Flat workbenches are essential for making moulding work. Modern benches are made from a sturdy steel frame and a thick plywood top that needs to be sealed with **shellac**. Traditional benches were built with brick or blocks and contained a solid plaster top bench that was costly and time consuming to construct.
Rubber bowls	Plaster is generally mixed by hand in flexible bowls that are easy to clean after use.

Shellac

Liquid material applied with a brush to seal porous surfaces and form a protective skin

As well as the above tools, other types of fine-bristle brushes are used to apply **release agents** and sealers used for preparing moulding work.

Release agent

A substance applied to the surface of a mould to ease its removal after the plaster has set

TYPES OF REVERSE MOULDS

There are four processes that can be used for making reverse moulds. Learning about these different processes will help you understand how and why they are chosen.

PLASTER REVERSE MOULD

A plaster reverse mould

When long, plain **cornice** mould is required, plaster reverse moulds are produced by running a plain run reverse section along the bench with the aid of a running mould. The profile of the plain run reverse makes the shape of the desired moulding. Before casting, the plaster reverse moulds will need to be sealed with shellac (see page 258), protecting the face and sealing the surface.

RUBBER REVERSE MOULD

A rubber reverse mould of a ceiling rose

Rubber reverse moulds are used to produce casts that contain enrichment or deep pattern undercut designs. A good example of this is an 'open flood' mould that is used to produce **ceiling roses** or wall plaques. The rubber reverse mould is flexible, allowing it to be easily removed after producing this type of moulding.

Before you use any type of rubber compound, you must read the risk assessment and manufacturer's instructions as rubber compound materials contain chemicals and toxins. The risk assessment and manufacturers' instructions will make you aware of any dangers that may exist, and of how these products should be disposed of safely. Using an extraction system is a good, safe way of extracting fumes, preventing inhalation of fumes from melting rubber or strong glues and hardeners.

Ceiling rose

A decorative, circular moulding attached to the ceiling, through which the electrical wires for a light pass

An extraction system

A section of flood mould with undercut design

A fence surrounding the model before pouring rubber compound

FIBREGLASS REVERSE MOULD

Fibreglass mould

Fibreglass reverse moulds can only be produced by applying the material over a model or a master copy of a mould. Fibreglass reverse moulds are strong and durable and will last much longer than plaster reverse moulds. They will not have the same detail and sharpness compared with a rubber compound mould and are best suited for making reverse moulds that are not undercut but have a plain face.

POSITIVE MOULD

A positive mould

Positive reverse moulds are mainly produced when running small panel mouldings or matching existing work. This could be done in order to repair a damaged cornice or dado moulding, for example. Positive moulds are made by first producing a template of the shape/design. This template is then fixed to a running mould. The constructed mould will be used to form the shape of the mould by running it on a bench against a timber rule.

Forming a positive mould

MATERIALS USED FOR PRODUCING MOULDINGS

You need to know about the different types of materials that are used to prepare and produce mouldings. The following section runs through them.

CASTING PLASTER

Class A plaster

A type of plaster that sets quickly and does not contain any retarder, unlike multi-finish plaster which has a retarder added to allow more working time

The main material used for producing fibrous casts is pure plaster; this is also known as 'plaster of Paris' and is a **class A plaster**. The most common type used for basic casting work is called 'casting plaster plus'. This plaster is preferred because it has a longer shelf life compared with the other types of casting plasters. Casting plaster has a fast set, normally with a working time of approximately 15 minutes, which means you need to be quick when using this plaster.

There are other types of casting plaster and each has its own specific use due to its characteristics and strength. Some casts need to be harder than others, especially if they are likely to suffer knocking or constant contact which can damage their surface.

The plaster needs to be stored in a dry area to get maximum use of the product.

HESSIAN

Roll of hessian

Hessian is a reinforcing canvas material that is sold in roll form. It can be incorporated within the cast to make it stronger and reduce cracking. A good pair of scissors or sharp knife can be used to cut this material.

FIBREGLASS STRANDS

Fibreglass strands can be added into the mix to reinforce the plaster.

Scissors can be used to cut hessian

A craft knife can also be used to cut hessian

Fibreglass strands for fibreglass moulds

Timber laths

TIMBER LATHS

These are used to provide a strong, rigid skeleton, preventing casts or mouldwork from snapping. Thick laths may draw moisture from casts, causing in-line cracks, so laths that are thicker than 3mm need to be soaked in water.

A container of shellac

Tallow
Rendered animal fat that, when mixed with paraffin at a ratio of 50:50, makes useable grease

SHELLAC

A liquid material that is applied with a brush to seal porous surfaces and form a protective skin, for example on plaster reverse moulds. Brushes that contain shellac need to be cleaned with methylated spirits.

PLASTERER'S GREASE

Applied by brush, grease is used as a release agent, allowing plaster casts to be removed with ease. **Tallow** is mixed with paraffin to make the grease.

SILICONE RELEASE AGENT

Sold in a canister, silicone-based release agents are sprayed onto background surfaces such as rubber and fibreglass to prolong their life span and act as a release agent.

Grease

Pliable
Easily bent and/or flexible

CLAY

Clay is a soft, **pliable** product that is used when running positive moulds. It is used to cover nail heads, and the plaster does not stick to it.

RETARDER

Retarder can be added to casting plaster to slow its setting time. This allows more working time when casting large casts before the plaster sets.

A silicone release agent spray

Clay

Retarder

RUBBER

There are two types of rubber used for producing reverse moulds.

Hot melt rubber

Hot melt rubber is available in solid form in hard-, medium- or soft-grade rubber. It needs to be melted in a thermostatically controlled melting pot or tank. The rubber material needs to be melted at approximately 140–170°C and poured when it is still at approximately 140–145°C. Always follow the manufacturer's guidelines for melting and pouring hot melt rubber as the temperatures may vary for different manufacturers.

When melting the rubber, a good extraction system must be used to remove the toxic fumes as they will be poisonous. Safety clothing must also be worn to protect you from the hot material and vapours when pouring the melted rubber.

The benefit of hot melt rubber is that it can be re-melted and re-used time and time again. However, you need expensive melting equipment and extraction systems to melt the rubber safely.

Porous models need to be sealed with a sealing agent or soaked in water before pouring rubber over their surface. A support case will be required due to the rubber shrinking and distorting after setting.

Cold pour rubber

Cold pour rubber compound is supplied in liquid form. It needs the addition of a hardener to make it set. In order to get the best results from the product, the manufacturer's guidelines must be followed when mixing cold pour compound, as it can be a costly and expensive procedure if things don't go to plan.

Cold pour rubber produces finer detail when producing reverse moulds and there is no need for a melting pot when preparing for a pour. However, you cannot re-use cold pour compound.

Rubber moulds

Hot melt rubber

ACTIVITY

Search the web for different melting appliances. Investigate:
- the quantity of rubber that they can melt
- the types and grade of rubber compounds that they can melt.

OUR HOUSE

Using 'Our House', complete the following tasks.
1 Design a cove-shape profile for a running mould for 'Our House'.
2 Measure the perimeter of the living room and work out a suitable length of reverse mould to be produced.
3 Work out how many casts you will require to go around the living room.

Cold pour rubber compound

CASTING

The process and procedure for casting can depend on factors such as:

- the size and shape of the cast
- its position (whether it is fixed inside or outside the building).

The majority of casts are made for internal features, so the cast can be made with casting plaster (which cannot be used for external use).

Before any casting takes place, you need to prepare the reverse mould.

Plaster reverse moulds are prepared by sealing them with several coats of shellac and followed by applying grease to the surface. At this stage, care must be taken not to leave heavy brush marks in the grease as this can affect the finished face after removing the cast.

Rubber moulds also need to be lubricated by spraying the surface with release agent. Plaster is a porous material when dry and, after time and constant casting, it will absorb the oils from the rubber compound.

Casting is a process that can be completed with either a 'one gauge' or 'two gauge' mix, depending on the size of the cast to be produced.

TWO GAUGE SYSTEM

The majority of casts are completed using the two gauge system, also known as **firstings and seconds**.

The 'firstings' is the first application of plaster. Its purpose is to prevent reinforcing materials from penetrating and showing through the face of the cast. The firstings is allowed to 'pull in' – this is the first stage of setting before applying the second mix.

The 'seconds' is the second mix which will have hessian and laths incorporated during the casting process. This makes the cast stronger, meaning you can use less plaster and therefore the cast lighter.

ONE GAUGE SYSTEM

Small casts are best cast with the one gauge system. This process involves mixing a gauge of plaster and partially applying it to the reverse mould. At this stage, **dryers** are applied before incorporating hessian and laths in a way that avoids them showing through the face of the cast. The remaining plaster is then applied, building up the back of the cast.

INDUSTRY TIP
After applying shellac, always clean brushes with methylated spirits.

INDUSTRY TIP
Always allow the shellac to dry before greasing.

Firstings and seconds
Two gauges of plaster used to cast moulds

INDUSTRY TIP
If using two gauges of plaster when casting, care must be taken to make sure that both mixes bond while tacky. If left to set, both mixes will separate.

Dryers
Dry plaster dust applied onto wet plaster to stiffen it

PRODUCING A CAST FROM A PLASTER REVERSE MOULD USING A TWO GAUGE SYSTEM

This is the step-by-step procedure for using the two gauge system to produce a cast from a plaster reverse mould.

Strike off

The built-up plaster area on the back of the cast which will come into contact with the background surface when fitted in place

STEP 1 Cut the hessian and laths to the required length.

STEP 2 Apply grease to the face of the reverse mould.

STEP 3 Mix the firstings.

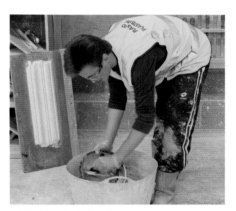

STEP 4 Apply the firstings to the reverse mould with a brush. Remove air from the cast by vibrating it, then leave it to pull in.

STEP 5 Wash the bowl as soon as possible, before the plaster sets.

STEP 6 Clean off the **strike off** before applying the seconds.

STEP 7 Mix the seconds and apply to the tacky firstings. Place the hessian/canvas in position, overhanging the strike offs.

STEP 8 Apply plaster over the hessian/canvas.

STEP 9 Bed the laths on the back of the cast.

STEP 10 Fold back the hessian/canvas over the laths to strengthen and reinforce the cast.

STEP 11 Build up the strike offs with the remaining plaster, then leave to set.

STEP 12 Use a lath to form the strike off.

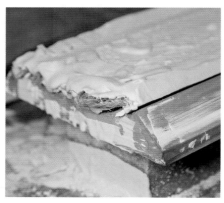

STEP 13 The cast will curl and lift slightly at both ends. However, it should not be removed until it has completely set.

ACTIVITY

Ask your tutor about the run cast method and how it is used for matching existing plaster mouldings.

If casting from rubber reverse moulds, silicone release agent must be applied instead of grease. The process and procedure for casting will be the same.

PREPARING A PLASTER MOULD FOR PRODUCING A FLOOD MOULD

You need to put on appropriate protective clothing and make sure safety equipment is working before starting this procedure. This will help protect you from fumes and the hot rubber compound.

STEP 1 Cut the rubber compound into smaller pieces using a utility knife. This will make it easier to melt.

STEP 2 Place the rubber compound into the melting pot and switch it on to melt the rubber.

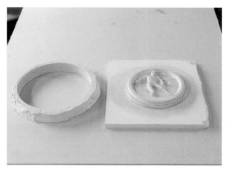

STEP 3 Prepare the mould by placing it on a flat surface, then make a fence around its position to hold the pouring rubber compound. The model can now be sealed.

STEP 4 Once the rubber has melted, it should be left to cool before it is poured. The melted rubber is poured allowing it to flow over the mould evenly, avoiding trapped air which can affect the face of the reverse mould. The rubber should be poured to below the fence level as this will need to be filled with plaster.

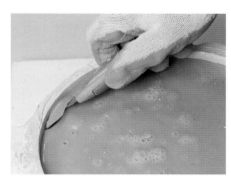

STEP 5 After it has set and cooled down, notch the rubber by cutting its edge with a utility knife, allowing the rubber to sit in the support case. Fill the back of the reverse mould with plaster to the top of the fence – this will form the case, allowing the mould to sit flat when producing a cast. Shellac the plaster support case once it is dry to seal the surface.

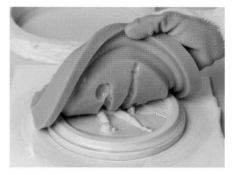

STEP 6 Remove the rubber compound mould.

STEP 7 The finished mould. This is now ready to be used to produce a cast, and remember to sit it on the plaster case.

EXTERIOR CASTS

Exterior casts are produced with sand and cement materials, using a semi-dry or wet method. The ratio of mix is normally 3 parts of sand and 1 part of cement (3:1).

An exterior gargoyle cast

Air void

Trapped air found in casts that have not been compacted during the casting process

Profile

The shape and pattern of the mould outline. The desired profile is normally outlined in the working drawing, unless you are matching an existing pattern from an original

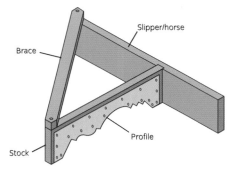

Parts of a running mould

- Semi-dry material contains little water and has to be compacted into moulds to make the cast. Smaller casts can be turned out more quickly than larger ones due to the weight, size and complexity of the design.

- The wet method requires a similar mix as render. This mix will contain more water and be far runnier. After pouring it into the cast, **air voids** will need to be removed by vibrating the mould.

Wet casts are slow setting and will need to be left in the reverse mould for at least 24 hours, allowing the mix to set hard, before they can be removed.

After setting, both types of casts need to be removed and left to cure. This curing process can take several days. Some casts are submerged in water, which helps to strengthen the cast.

Some good examples of external moulding work are balustrades, copings or gargoyles, which are used to decorate the exterior of buildings.

POSITIVE MOULDS

When producing moulds, an alternative to casting is to run and form a positive mould on a bench; this does not require a reverse.

Running moulds are constructed from timber. They have a zinc or aluminium template which forms the **profile** shape of the moulding.

CONSTRUCTING A POSITIVE RUNNING MOULD

Before you start making your running mould, you need to gather the following tools:

- a hand saw for cutting timber to the required size
- a coping saw for cutting out the profile line on the stock
- a hammer for fixing the timber parts
- tin snips and files for cutting the zinc or aluminium template
- a tape measure and a pencil
- a square.

The following steps show you how to construct a running mould.

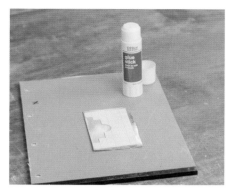

STEP 1 Design the basic shape of the profile on graph paper and stick it onto a piece of aluminium or zinc.

STEP 2 Cut out the shape of the profile with tin snips to within 2mm of the profile line.

STEP 3 Use a file to file away finish up to the profile line.

STEP 4 Any burrs can be removed with **wet and dry abrasive paper**.

STEP 5 Cut your stock. This should be wider and longer than the profile metal (5mm bigger in both directions) in order to fit the profile on its surface. This allows for any swelling that might occur when in contact with wet plaster. Fix your aluminium/zinc profile to the stock using tacks.

STEP 6 The stock and profile can now be fixed to the 'slipper'. For strength, the stock can be notched, then glued and screwed into position. Make sure that the stock and slipper sit flat on the bench before fixing them together. For stability when running on the bench, it is normal for the slipper to be longer than the stock.

STEP 7 Braces can be fixed to support the stock and slipper. Use a square to make sure the stock is set at a right angle to the slipper before fixing.

STEP 8 The running mould has been constructed but you may want to seal the timber with shellac before it comes into contact with wet plaster. This will increase the running mould's life span and prevent distortion of the timber.

Wet and dry abrasive paper

Abrasive paper, made from silicon carbide, may be used either dry or with water, which reduces clogging

A running rule fixed straight along the length of the bench

The next stage is to set up the bench to run and form the positive mould.

RUNNING A POSITIVE MOULD ON THE BENCH

Before you run a positive mould, you need to prepare your equipment. This includes gathering water buckets for cleaning and bowls for mixing. The bench surface will need to be shellaced and greased, and a running rule should be fixed straight and parallel along the length of the bench.

STEP 1 Fix nails at the centre along the run of the mould.

STEP 2 Cover the nails with clay to prevent the mould from moving and coming away from the bench. This can happen when the plaster swells.

STEP 3 Mix the casting plaster.

STEP 4 Apply the mixed plaster along the length of the run.

STEP 5 Hold the running mould firmly with both hands and run it along the timber rule, forming the shape of the mould.

STEP 6 Use the joint rule to remove excess plaster.

STEP 7 Wash the mould.

STEP 8 Repeat the process several times, building up the positive mould.

STEP 9 Build up the mould further.

STEP 10 Once the mould has been completed, it should be left to set hard. It can then be removed from the bench to be stored on a flat surface to avoid it bowing out of shape.

FIXING CASTS

Completed casts are sometimes placed in a purposely heated room to speed up the drying process, or they can be left to dry naturally at room temperature which can be time consuming. Once dry, the weight of the casts is reduced (as the water has evaporated), making them lighter but stronger for fixing to walls and ceilings.

Information about the installation and fixing procedures for plaster mouldings will vary from job to job and will be outlined in the specification.

The way the cast or positive mould is fixed will depend on its weight and the background it is being fixed to. Lighter moulds are fixed with adhesive, while larger moulds are fixed with mechanical fixings. Plaster moulds that are fixed with adhesive need to be scored on the contact surface to improve the key and then sealed with diluted PVA

PVA

to reduce suction. The background surface will also need to be prepared in the same way; this will improve the bond between the cast and background.

Manufacturers' guidelines and instructions should be followed when using either fixing adhesive or mechanical fixings. This will ensure that the work is completed to the required standards.

CALCULATING QUANTITIES

As with all plasterwork, for fibrous plastering you need to be able to calculate the amount of plaster needed. Below is an example for plain ceiling roses.

Example

To calculate the amount of casting plaster required for a ceiling rose, you first need to work out the total volume of the ceiling rose. Use the following formula, which is based on the formula for calculating the volume of a cylinder:

$\pi r^2 \times$ height

To work out the area of the ceiling rose, follow the process below.

Step 1

Measure the diameter of the ceiling rose. The diameter is the length of a straight line going through the centre of a circle connecting two points. In this example, the diameter is 1.75m.

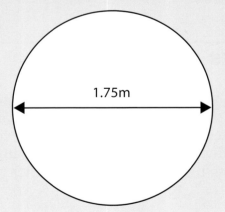

1.75m

Step 2

The radius (r) is half the diameter. To work out the radius, divide the diameter by 2.

1.75m ÷ 2 = 0.875m

Step 3

Next you need to work out the height of the cylinder (or in this example, the thickness of the rose). In this example, the height is 0.12m.

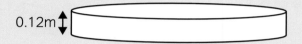

0.12m

π (3.142) is then multiplied by r^2 and by the height. This will give you the total cubic metres (m^3). So in this example the calculation is:

$3.142 × 0.875^2 × 0.12 = 0.2886m^3$

So the total volume of the ceiling rose to be plastered is **$0.2886m^3$**.

Case Study: Stuart and Ben

Stuart and Ben were working on a Victorian house, renovating some defective plasterwork, when they noticed that the panel mould on the ceiling had missing members.

Stuart and Ben explained to the owner that while they were repairing the plasterwork it would make sense to also repair the panel mould. They would be able to repair and make good the damage so that the owner could redecorate. Before giving them the go-ahead, the owner asked Stuart to explain the process for repairing the mould.

Stuart explained to the owner that he would need to cut through the mould with a saw and then place a piece of card into the cut section to take a profile of the mould design. Once he had the profile, he could transfer it to an aluminium template and cut out the outline of the mould profile. Then he could then fix the template to a stock and construct a running mould. The panel mould would need to be run on a bench in the garage and left to dry before fixing it into position.

Before fixing the moulding, Stuart would need to make clean cuts to both ends of the damaged panel mould and remove the defective area with a hammer and sharp wood chisel, tools chosen to cause as little vibration and impact as possible in an attempt to avoid further damage.

The final process would be to bed the mould back into position, using a joint rule to line the moulding members and making good where the new pieces met the old using casting plaster applied with a small tool and busk.

The owner was happy with Stuart's explanation and gave him and Ben the go-ahead to do the extra work.

Work through the following questions to check your learning.

1 Which one of the following classes of plaster is used for fibrous plastering?

   a   A.

   b   B.

   c   C.

   d   D.

2 Casting plaster sets within how many minutes?

   a   15.

   b   30.

   c   45.

   d   60.

3 Which one of the following moulds are plaster casts taken from?

   a   Reverse.

   b   Run.

   c   Running.

   d   Finished.

4 Plaster casts are reinforced with

   a   tape

   b   hessian

   c   steel

   d   plastic.

5 Which one of the following materials is plasterer's grease made from?

   a   Plaster and paraffin.

   b   Paraffin and shellac.

   c   Beef dripping and shellac.

   d   Tallow and paraffin.

6 Shellac is used to

   a   seal the surface

   b   decorate the surface

   c   clean the mould

   d   cure the mould.

7 Models are required for reverse moulds that contain undercut sections. Which one of the following is the **best** material to use?

   a   Solid plaster.

   b   Softer plaster.

   c   Rubber compound.

   d   Silicone sealant.

8 Melting pots are used to prepare

   a   plastic compound

   b   rubber compound

   c   reverse run

   d   positive run.

9 Which one of the following is **best** used to form plaster reverse moulds?

   a   Running moulds.

   b   Fibreglass reverse moulds.

   c   Hot melt compound.

   d   Cold pour compound.

10 A two gauge process used for casting will include

   a   firstings only

   b   secondings only

   c   firstings and seconds

   d   firsts, seconds and thirds.

11 Retarder is added to plaster in order to

a   increase the set

b   increase the strength

c   slow down the set

d   weaken the strength.

12 What type of hand tool is used for cutting hessian?

a   Saw.

b   Busk.

c   Joint rule.

d   Scissors.

13 Which one of the following processes uses dryers when producing casts?

a   One gauge.

b   Two gauge.

c   Three gauge.

d   Four gauge.

14 Laths incorporated in casts will increase the

a   shelf life

b   setting times

c   strength

d   span.

15 When melting rubber compound, extraction systems are used to remove

a   moisture

b   warm air

c   fumes

d   dust.

16 Casts produced for external fixing will be made from

a   finishing plaster

b   casting plaster

c   lightweight plaster

d   sand and cement.

17 Plaster models are prepared with

a   size

b   grease

c   shellac sealer

d   silicone sealant.

18 Which one of the following surfaces are positive moulds run on?

a   Plywood.

b   Slate.

c   Plastic.

d   Fibreglass.

19 Which one of the following mix ratios is used for external castings?

a   4 parts sand:1 part cement.

b   4 parts sand:2 parts cement.

c   3 parts cement:1 part sand.

d   3 parts sand:1 part cement.

20 Large casts are fixed to solid backgrounds using

a   galvanised nails

b   steel nails

c   dry wall screws

d   screws and plugs.

TEST YOUR KNOWLEDGE ANSWERS

Chapter 1: Unit 201

1   c   Risk assessment.
2   d   Blue circle.
3   b   Oxygen.
4   a CO_2.
5   b   Control of Substances Hazardous to Health (COSHH) Regulations 2002.
6   c   75°.
7   c   Glasses, hearing protection and dust mask.
8   d   Respirator.
9   a   410V.
10 b   80dB(a).

Chapter 2: Unit 101

1   c   15m.
2   a   open to interpretation
3   b   A section through a part of the structure.
4   a   Strip.
5   c   Raft.
6   c   Damp proof course.
7   d   Polystyrene.
8   d   cement.
9   b   10°
10 a   foundations

Chapter 3: Unit 121

1   d   applying water to the surface.
2   a   a solution of PVA mixed with water
3   c   a high-suction background
4   a   Claw hammer.
5   d   cement mix.
6   a   pointing hammer

7   c   Timber wall plates.
8   b   scabbling tool
9   a   Bucket, water, powder, mix and empty.
10 d   powered drill and whisk.
11 d   with dirty water.
12 c   mechanical drum mixer
13 b   different strength of mix
14 a   increase its strength
15 b   Improve the adhesion properties of the mix.
16 a   pre-mixed plaster
17 c   sea sand
18 b   a production date
19 d   workability.
20 a   At the start of the mixing process.

Chapter 4: Unit 122

1   c   Three.
2   a   uneven backgrounds
3   c   penetrating damp
4   a   comb scratcher
5   c   adhesion and suction
6   a   Cement.
7   c   setting times
8   c   Glasses.
9   c   specification
10 a   drawing
11 c   Straight edge.
12 a   scratch coat
13 c   Float and set.
14 d   too thickly.
15 c   diagonally
16 b   allow the next coat to bond

17 d 10mm.

18 b mechanical drum mixer

19 b bucket

20 d compatible.

Chapter 5: Unit 123

1 d 12.5mm.

2 c Expanded metal lathing.

3 a speeds up the build process

4 c Tin snips.

5 b 32mm.

6 d to reduce the risk of cracking.

7 b 300mm.

8 b driven in at an angle

9 c school corridors

10 d Scrim.

11 a keep it tight

12 b rusting

13 d Thin render stop.

14 d bending.

15 c time to change the pad saw's blade

16 c reduce the risk of cracking

17 b galvanised clout nails

18 b Pink.

19 d Hacksaw and tin snips.

20 b 3mm.

Chapter 6: Unit 124

1 c Bonding.

2 b Devil float.

3 a Perlite.

4 a the angles should always be cut out

5 a Spirit level.

6 b Sand.

7 c 10–12mm.

8 b Plaster will crack.

9 d Trowel float trowel.

10 a Straight edge.

11 b Plasterboard.

12 c Sand.

13 a Cement.

14 c Sand.

15 a Plaster.

16 b Prepare the background.

17 a Trowel.

18 b Class B.

19 a 1½–2 hours.

20 d 2–3mm.

Chapter 7: Unit 125

1 d B retarded hemihydrate.

2 a Coarse.

3 a cold and clean

4 b Two times.

5 b 2.

6 b 110V.

7 a Fat.

8 a Gaul.

9 d Floating coat.

10 d Use by.

11 a 40.

12 b flash set

13 c Gurnished.

14 d It will be difficult to decorate.

15 b quicker

16 c Devil float.

17 c 2mm.

18 c Top left.

19 b Spot board and stand.

20 c Finishing trowel.

Chapter 8

1 a 3:1.

2 b Finished floor level.

3 a scabbling

4 a Coarse sharp.

5 d Laitance.

6 c PVA and cement.

7 b Three hours.

8 c To slow down the set.

9 a A set point from which to take levels.

10 c Unbonded.

11 a datum line

12 c Ordinary Portland.

13 b Sweep clean, apply grout and thoroughly soak.

14 c Floating.

15 b To allow for drainage.

16 c Semi-dry.

17 b level

18 d Bonded.

19 b To allow cement to fully harden.

20 a Cover with a polythene sheet.

Chapter 9

1 a A.

2 a 15.

3 a Reverse.

4 b hessian

5 d Tallow and paraffin.

6 a seal the surface

7 c Rubber compound.

8 b rubber compound

9 a Running moulds.

10 c firstings and seconds

11 c slow down the set

12 d Scissors.

13 a One gauge.

14 c strength

15 c fumes

16 d sand and cement.

17 d silicone sealant.

18 a Plywood.

19 d 3 parts sand:1 part cement.

20 d screws and plugs.

INDEX

wastage 56
measured quantities 54
measurement, units of 57
mechanical breakers xxiv, 110–112
mechanical drum mixer 125
melanoma 23
method statement xxiv, 7
mixing stand xxiv, 123
mixing 124–129
   area 124
   finish plasters 217–220
   ratios 127, 142, 147
   test mixing 149
mortar xxiv, 85, 119
multifoil 95

N

nails 168–169
nodules xxiv, 215
noise levels 20, 33

O

one coat work 190
operatives 14
Ordinary Portland Cement (OPC) xxiv, 115, 194
Ordnance bench mark (OBM) 47

P

pad foundations 80
pad saw xxiv, 167
paddle mixer 218
pan mixer xxv, 240
paper tape 173
pencil 167
percentages 62
perimeter xxv
   calculating 130
perlite xxv, 144, 191
personal hygiene 34
personal protective equipment (PPE) xxv, 4
Personal Protective Equipment (PPE) at Work Regulations 1992 4, 20–23
pi 68

pile foundations 80
PIR (polyisocyanurate) 95
pitched roofs 89
plaster
   class A xvii, 193, 256
   class B 193, 214
   green xxi
   see also mixing; storage
plasterboards xxxii, 103, 160–161
   building regulations 164
   cutting for electrical boxes 176–177
   faults 169–171
   fixing to ceilings 177
   fixing to stud walls 173–177
   fixings 164, 168–169
   handling 166
   jointing 161, 171–173
   measuring 160
   staggering joints 170–171
   storing 165
   types of 163–165
   waste disposal 112, 178
plastering trowel xxv, 140
plasticiser 85, 121, 195
plated drywall screw xxv, 169
platforms 168
plug, wiring 36
plumb dot and screed 198–200
plunger xxv, 122
pointing hammer xxvi, 109
polyvinyl acetate (PVA) xxvi
popping 169
portable appliance testing (PAT) 37
positive moulds 256, 264–267
power tools 37, 110–112
PPE see personal protective equipment (PPE)
preambles 54
pre-cast concrete 143
pre-cast plasterwork 250–251
pre-formed beads 178–180, 183–186
   fixing 185–186
pre-mixed plaster 118, 122, 129, 143
pre-plastering tests 115
prefabricated walling 87

preliminaries 54
preparation see background surfaces
pricing for work 146
pricking up coat 145
principle contractor 14
profile xxvi
programme of work xxxiv
prohibition notice xxvi, 8
prohibition signs 41
prop 177
Provision and Use of Work Equipment Regulations (PUWER) 1998 16–17
PVA (polyvinyl acetate) 115
Pythagorean theorem 66

Q

quantities, calculating 55–70

R

radius 68
raft foundations 81
raking joints 107
ratio for mixing 127, 142, 147
release agents xxvii, 253, 258
Reporting of Injuries, Diseases and Dangerous Occurrences Regulations (RIDDOR) 2013 12
requisition order 73
respirators 23
rest areas 16
retarders xxvii, 193, 258
reverse moulds xxvii, 250–251, 254–256, 261–262
risk assessment 5–6
roofs 88
rotary kiln xxvii, 194
rubber 259
rubber bowls 253

S

safe condition signs 42
safety see health and safety
safety glasses 22
safety helmet 22
safety notices 41–42

V

variation order 72
verbal communication 75
vermiculite xxxiv, 103, 192
vibration white finger (VWF) 23, 31, 110–111
volatile organic compounds (VOC) 10
voltages 35, 110, 218
volume, calculating 69–70

W

wall plates xxxiv, 182
walling 83–84
    external 84–87
    internal 87–88
    see also background surfaces
washing facilities 15
washing hands 34
wastage 56
waste disposal 112–113, 178
water
    drinking 16
    services 90–91
water level xxxiv, 235
water power 97
waterproofer 148, 195–196
welfare facilities 15–16
Well's disease 12
wheelbarrow 141
wide strip foundations 79
wind power 96–97
wire brush xxxiv, 110
wiring a plug 36
wooden laths xxxiv, 160
Work at Height Regulations 2005 (as amended) 24–30
work equipment *see* equipment
work schedules xxxiv, 55
workbench xx
written communication 71–74

PICTURE CREDITS